VICTORIA GOWRAMMA

The Lost Princess of Coorg

VICTORIA GOWRAMMA
The Lost Princess of Coorg

C.P. Belliappa

Rupa & Co

Typeset by
Mindways Design
1410 Chiranjiv Tower
43 Nehru Place
New Delhi 110 019

Printed in India by
Rekha Printers Pvt. Ltd.
A-102/1 Okhla Industrial Area, Phase-II
New Delhi-110 020

CONTENTS

AUTHOR'S NOTE

I HAVE BEEN fascinated with the extraordinary life of Victoria Gowramma, an Indian princess from Coorg—a province dwarfed by the immense size of India—and the incredible attention she received from Queen Victoria, the sovereign of the most powerful colonial power in the world.

Princess Victoria Gowramma landed in England in May 1852 along with her father, Veerarajendra—the last raja of Coorg. Both father and daughter spent the rest of their lives on English soil. However, except for fleeting details very little of their life in England was known. There were references to a few books written during the late nineteenth century which are now out of print. I desperately sought these memoirs, especially: *Lady Login's Recollections, Coorg and its Rajahs,* and *Private Letters of Marquees of Dalhousie.* I finally found them at a place I least expected them—on the worldwide web!

My thanks, therefore, primarily goes to that amazing invention: the search engine Google. Sitting in my little room in Coorg, typical rural India, I could access documents from archives in far-flung countries. I was able to download entire books on to my computer. For me, it was nothing short of serendipity.

During my surfing-the-net, there was another serendipitous discovery. I stumbled on the archives of *The Times, London.* I took a month's subscription and was hugely rewarded with first-hand recordings of some of the important events in the lives of Princess Victoria Gowramma, Veerarajendra, and Maharaja Duleep Singh. With this hitherto unpublished information, I was able to reconstruct the years the protagonists of this book had spent in England, and the unbelievable importance given to them in the court of Queen Victoria.

One more chance discovery was the existence of a marble bust of Princess Victoria Gowramma. It was ecstasy when I tracked it to the Royal Collections in Osborne House, the favourite retreat of Queen Victoria. With permission from: The Royal Collection © 2009 Her Majesty Queen Elizabeth II, I have used the unique painted marble bust of Princess Victoria Gowramma on the cover of this book. This image has not been seen since it was sculpted by Baron Carlo Marochetti in 1856.

By the time I was half-way through writing the book, there was another lucky revelation. I learnt that a private art collector in Bangalore had recently acquired the Bible which Queen Victoria presented to her goddaughter, Victoria Gowramma, on the day of the princess's baptism in Buckingham Palace. It was an incredible experience for me to hold this Bible, so relevant to what I was covering. I thank Mr A. Franklin and his wife

Sharmela for permitting me to photograph this rare artifact and to reproduce the images in my book.

I am grateful to Dr Praveen Sirdesai, a direct descendent of Veerarajendra for information about the raja's family. My thanks to Lady Moni Forman for a rare sketch of one of Veerarajendra's wives commissioned during the raja's stay in London.

I thank my brothers-in-law Brig. (Retd.) K.M. Muthanna and Mr Vijay Nambisan, sisters Mrs Vijaya Muthanna and Dr Kavery Nambisan for their valuable suggestions and help.

This is my third book with Rupa & Co. I am indebted to publisher Mr Kapish Mehra of Rupa & Co., for his support and encouragement. I thank my Editor Ms Rashmi Menon and her assistant Mr Ankush for their suggestions and efforts in editing the manuscript.

My wife Aruna, son Vikram and daughter-in-law Dechu have been highly supportive. I gratefully acknowledge their help.

Coorg
July 2009   C.P. Belliappa

PREFACE

ON THE LAST day of the sixteenth century, the British East India Company was awarded the coveted royal charter from Queen Elizabeth to trade in the East Indies, especially India, that was then dominated by the Dutch and the Portuguese. The Company wanted the patronage of the British sovereign to facilitate their business plans of importing spices, cotton and other raw materials from the Indian subcontinent, in exchange for textiles, steel, and industrial products churned out by their factories in London, Manchester, and Leeds.

Around the time these events were unfolding that would usher in momentous changes in far away India, a young Lingayat prince named Veeraraja from the Ikkeri dynasty in the present-day state of Karnataka in southern India, sought permission from one of the nayakas or warlords in neighbouring Kodagu (Coorg) to establish a Lingayat religious mission, *jangamvadi*, in a small hamlet named Haleri.

While the East India Company exploited the rivalry between the local rulers to establish British supremacy in the Indian subcontinent, Veeraraja took advantage of the hopelessly divided nayakas of Kodagu to establish the Haleri dynasty in the thickly forested hilly region spread over 1500 square miles. His successors consolidated the dynasty's hold on Kodagu by vanquishing all the nayakas, and ruled the land for more than two centuries by winning the support of the indigenous martial race, the Kodavas or the Coorgs. The Haleri rajas fortified their bond with the Coorgs by forging several marriage alliances between the two communities. The Haleri rajas belonged to the Siva-worshipping Lingayat sect, which was alien to Kodagu. The Kodavas, the local inhabitants, mainly worshipped nature and their forefathers. The brazen determination exhibited by a few brave and audacious men, from a country seven-thousand miles away, in taking control of India, was replicated albeit on a lesser scale by the Haleri rajas in establishing their realm in Kodagu.

The paths of the British East India Company and the rajas of the Haleri dynasty crossed during Hyder Ali's reign in neighbouring Mysore. Hyder Ali, and later his son Tipu Sultan, understood the strategic importance of Kodagu in keeping the British at bay from attacking their domain from the western flank. Hyder Ali and Tipu Sultan made several forays into the inhospitable terrain of Kodagu to take over the land, but failed to gain total control. Unable to subdue the indomitable Kodavas, they held Kodagu tenuously from 1780 to 1791. The heir to the throne, Veerarajendra (popularly known as Dodda Veerarajendra) was imprisoned by Tipu, and attempts were made to forcibly convert him to Islam. In

1788, with help from his Kodava subjects, Veerarajendra escaped. He fought Tipu for the next three years to regain his kingdom. It was during this period that the British approached the young Dodda Veerarajendra for a strategic partnership to defeat their common enemy—Tipu Sultan. The British East India Company recognised the importance of Coorg in their design to eliminate the powerful Tipu Sultan. They secured a foothold in Coorg by signing a friendship treaty with the raja of Kodagu in 1790. Both Dodda Veerarajendra and the British benefitted from this alliance, and Tipu was vanquished in the last Mysore war of 1799.

Dodda Veerarajendra's brother and successor, Lingarajendra, continued the friendship with the British. It was during the reign of his son, also named Veerarajendra (popularly referred to as Chikka Veerarajendra), that the relationship between the raja of Kodagu and the British soured. Chikka Veerarajendra's confrontation with the British started in 1830 and came to a head during 1834. His atrocities against the Kodavas alienated his subjects to a point where they supported the British in taking over the administration of the kingdom. Kodagu thus became a part of British territory, and Chikka Veerarajendra was exiled from his kingdom in April 1834. Chikka Veerarajendra and his family were first taken to Vellore where they spent about a year. He was then relocated to Benares in 1836.

This book deals with Chikka Veerarajendra's life in Benares and his remarkable journey to England in 1852 along with his eleven-year-old daughter, Gowramma. He was the first deposed Indian ruler to be granted permission to sail to Britain. The reason the East India Company agreed was mainly because Veerarajendra wished his daughter to be raised as a Christian and given a Western education. Queen Victoria, Governor-General

Lord Dalhousie, and the evangelical British officers saw great potential in converting a member of an Indian royal family to Christianity. However, Veerarajendra had his own motives for travelling to England.

In London, Queen Victoria espoused unprecedented interest in Gowramma and accepted the princess as her goddaughter. After her baptism, Gowramma was given the name 'Victoria' by the queen. Two years later, in 1854, Maharaja Duleep Singh of Punjab converted to Christianity at Fatehgarh. Anxious to prevent the sixteen-year-old maharaja from becoming a rallying force for the Sikhs, he was encouraged by the British to pursue his education in England. Impressed by the young maharaja, whose enormous wealth was now a part of the British Crown, Queen Victoria and Prince Albert were keen that Duleep Singh be treated with dignity. At the queen's behest, he was given a status equivalent to that enjoyed by the European princes.

Serious efforts were also made to bring about an alliance between these two juvenile Christian royals from India. It was hoped that a union between Maharaja Duleep Singh and Princess Victoria Gowramma would act as a catalyst in encouraging voluntary conversion to Christianity amongst the upper castes in India, especially the Hindu rulers. It was projected that within two decades, there could be a large number of Christian-born Indian royals; once the process was set in motion, the figures would grow exponentially. For the evangelists, there was the delightful possibility of eventually a predominant Christian India emerging, which would owe allegiance to the Church of England. It was argued that the success of this scheme would have great impact on the subcontinent, and the outcome was expected to be historic.

What better binding force than Christianity to peacefully bring the diverse citizens of India under the colonial masters?

The two Indian bluebloods thus became pawns in a grand scheme. Nevertheless, Queen Victoria was genuinely fond of her young Indian friend, Maharaja Duleep Singh, and goddaughter Princess Gowramma. She bestowed on them unprecedented access to socialise with her family. Though Queen Victoria was known for her prudishness, she was surprisingly lenient and forgiving with her occasionally truant oriental royal subjects. However, this unusual saga ended with great disappointments all around.

This book is embellished with a number of relevant letters, excerpts, and quotes from various publications of the period. These have been reproduced verbatim since they support the story more succinctly. However, the currently popular spellings such as Gowramma, Veerarajendra, raja, and maharaja have been used in the main text of the book. Readers will also find that whenever Queen Victoria, Lord Dalhousie, and other notables wrote, they referred to themselves by their own names or titles, as was the norm those days.

In order to keep the flow of the story, a certain amount of dramatising has been introduced. These extrapolations have been carried out keeping intact the historical facts and occurrences.

1

A PRINCESS IS BORN

*I*T WAS JULY 1841. The belated monsoon showers had settled the dust and cooled the oppressive summer heat in north India. Chikka Veerarajendra, the deposed raja of Kodagu, sat brooding in the large carved rosewood chair, a poor replica of the ornate throne he once sat upon, as had his father, Lingarajendra, and his uncle, the powerful Dodda Veerarajendra. He hated the prefix 'Chikka' to his name that meant 'small' or 'junior'. His uncle and namesake had the more flattering 'Dodda' or 'senior' affixed to his name. Dodda Veerarajendra was the acknowledged hero of the Haleri dynasty that had ruled Kodagu for well over two centuries, i.e., from 1600 to 1834. The senior Veerarajendra had valiantly fought Hyder Ali and Tipu Sultan to regain their appropriated kingdom and had allied with the British East India Company in the last Mysore war of 1799, which brought to an end Tipu's reign.

Chikka Veerarajendra, after suffering a humiliating defeat at the hands of the white man, had been unceremoniously deported to far away Benares. Here he was, in exile, held hostage in a haveli. He had lost the beautiful kingdom of Kodagu, painstakingly built by his ancestors, to the East India Company, who was his dynasty's professed friend and ally. The haveli that he now occupied, though spacious, could hardly be compared to the opulent palace where each of his thirteen wives had independent chambers. Two of his wives were now in labour, and were sharing the same room in this house that his captors had sardonically named 'Coorg Nest'. He disliked the name Coorg given by the *feringhees* to his lush mountainous kingdom of Kodagu.

Just thinking about his beloved Kodagu, especially in the unbearable heat of the north, made Chikka Veerarajendra dejected. In Kodagu, it was salubrious all through the year and the lush greenery sprung to life during the torrential monsoon rains. All his surviving twelve wives constantly complained of the extreme weather of the north. Seven years in Benares seemed like an eternity, and none in his entourage had become accustomed to the severe summer and the bone-chilling winter. Benares, the hub of Hindu pilgrimage, was forever teeming with humanity—noisy, dusty, and chaotic—which he and his wives could never get accustomed to. Of his thirteen wives who had accompanied him when he was deposed and exiled on that fateful day in 1834, one had died during their ten months of captivity in Vellore.

Veerarajendra had an infant son named Chitrashekara when he was forced to leave his realm. In the last seven years, his family had grown. He was now thirty-nine year old, and had already fathered six sons and a daughter. His children were the only ones who did not complain about the weather. He deeply resented his fate; he was reduced to doing nothing but produce children. He now awaited the addition of two more children. However, one of his pregnant wives, and his royal consort, Devammaji, was not in good health. Captain T.D. Carpenter, the agent appointed by the British East India Company to manage the affairs of the Raja, had arranged for a British doctor to examine Devammaji. The doctor had said: 'I am sorry, Your Highness. The rani has serious complications. In all likelihood, neither the mother nor the child is likely to survive the ordeal.' Veerarajendra was therefore full of foreboding for the events about to unfold.

By nightfall, Coorg Nest was the scene of hectic activities. Both the women were close to accouchement. Midwives scurried around the dimly-lit rooms. Kaverammaji, another wife of the raja, had served him dinner but he could barely eat. Being in a depressed state for several months, Veerarajendra's once-muscular figure had turned gaunt. Kaverammaji tried her best to comfort him and beseeched: 'Mahaswami, your good health and well-being is paramount for us all. Please help us to take care of you.' But Veerarajendra remained silent.

From one of the nearby rooms, he could hear the agonising screams of labour. Devammaji was very dear to him, and of all his wives, he was most comfortable in her company. She was a great lover: an enchantress with an endearing sense of humour. Only in her presence could he forget the miserable events that had led him to eventually lose his kingdom. He repented not having heeded her advice during his confrontation with the British. She had advised him to release the British East India Company's representative, Kullapally Karunakara Menon, whom the raja had recklessly taken hostage. Devammaji had pleaded with him to set free the emissary of the Company in order to defuse the tension with the powerful British. His senior court official, Dewan Ponnappa, too had proffered the same advice. Instead, Veerarajendra made the monumental blunder of embarking on a collision course with the white man. His judgement had been clouded by the exaggerated confidence and invincibility projected by the sycophant Dewan Kunta Basava and that unscrupulous *mussalman* in his court, Abbas Ali.

Veerarajendra pondered about his fate and the future. Devammaji's health had deteriorated ever since she had conceived the child. This would be his favourite consort's first child, even though they had been married for twelve years. Veerarajendra felt responsible for her suffering, and dreaded the thought of losing her. 'If Devammaji's child is a male, the infant will be the heir to the throne,' he thought. Bemused, he heard himself mumble, 'What throne?'

The sacred river Ganges flowed not too far from his abode. He had taken each of his wives for a dip in the holy river, offered prayers and performed elaborate *poojas*. He hoped his transgressions would be washed away and that he would soon return to his kingdom to re-establish the sovereignty of the Haleri dynasty. He occupied two large rooms on the first floor of the haveli. Each of his wives took turns to co-habit with him two weeks at a time, depending on their biological conditions. During this period, children by the wife-in-favour were allowed to occupy the spare room.

He had servants, cooks and attendants who had accompanied him from Coorg. The raja's small entourage now included three eunuchs to guard his women and to decide who would spend time with their lord. The 60,000 rupees of pension that the British doled out to Veerarajendra every year from the revenues earned in his erstwhile kingdom was a pittance. He felt insulted at receiving this paltry sum from the feringhees. It afforded him a comfortable living, but without all the power, pomp and luxury that he was born into and had enjoyed. He cursed the white man and their Company for illegally usurping his kingdom and confiscating his wealth. When it had become certain that he was to be deprived of his treasures and exiled, he had instructed his wives to collect as much of the valuables they could, and stitch them on to their undergarments, in addition to wearing substantial quantities of jewellery on their person. They had barely two days to complete this task. His wives had walked with difficulty, weighed down by the heavy burden. He had also managed to retrieve some of his valuable possessions in the form of jewellery, gems, ivory, gold and silver coins shrewdly hidden in the personal effects of his wives and other women who were carried in fifty palanquins, as they left Madikeri, his capital. Here again, the British had corrupted the name of the capital established by his ancestor Mudduraja, from Madikeri to Mercara. Tears filled his eyes at the memory of the day he and his family had to leave Madikeri ignominiously.

Veerarajendra shifted in his chair as images of his exit from Kodagu came to haunt him again. He felt ridiculous for having imprudently asked the palace band to play the celebratory march-past 'The British Grenadier' as he came out of the Madikeri palace riding his favourite elephant. The British agent, Colonel James S. Fraser had arranged a twenty-one-gun salute for him. He had failed to grasp the contempt in that mock show of respect by his captors. He was totally confused at the time, and had made desperate attempts to please the British. He remembered his subjects lining the street to see him, and the caravan of palanquins and bullock-carts exit the fort for the last time. In a bid to put on a brave front, he had chosen to sit in the silver-clad *howdah* perched on the elephant. To make it appear like a royal procession, he had dressed in his ceremonial brocade coat tied at the waist with a *chele*, the traditional Coorg sash, and the Turkish-fez-shaped cap embellished with diamonds and precious gems, perched on his head.

He had noticed that not all his subjects were sorry to see him banished from his kingdom. While a number of them stood silently with folded hands, and some women wailed, he also heard snide remarks about him and his wives. He could not forget one of them mockingly yell: 'Looks like all the wives of the raja are pregnant!' This comment was prompted because the palanquin bearers were struggling with the additional burden of the treasure they were carrying.

Colonel Fraser had confiscated most of the valuable assets in the treasury of the raja amounting to sixteen lakh rupees. Veerarajendra and his entourage were allowed to take their personal effects and just 10,000 rupees for the journey. He remembered the first camp where they had to pitch tents en route to Bangalore. It had rained and the palanquin bearers found it extremely difficult to carry the heavy palanquins. Many of the palanquin carriers abandoned the camp at night. Somehow or the other, Veerarajendra had to hide the treasure they could no longer carry. Along with his wives, and with assistance from a few of his loyal servants, they buried substantial quantities of the treasure in hurriedly-dug pits within the confines of the tent. The women, however, sighed in relief for having shed the weight of some of the jewellery attached to their petticoats. Two of his wives had bruises caused by the sharp edges of the concealed ornaments. Veerarajendra hoped to return one day to recover the cache. However, while at Vellore Fort as prisoner, visitors from Kodagu had informed him that the British had got wind of the buried riches and had unearthed most of them. The thought always made him abuse the feringhees in the choicest of expletives.

It was close to midnight when Veerarajendra was suddenly jolted from his painful ruminations by the piercing scream of Devammaji. He also heard a feeble cry of the newborn. It was Sunday, 4 July 1841. One of the eunuchs came a little later to announce that Devammaji had given birth to a girl child. Veerarajendra was visibly disappointed at the news. Both Devammaji and he had wanted a son. Just then, a maidservant rushed in to state that the rani's health had taken a turn for the worse.

By the time Veerarajendra entered the room where Devammaji lay, she was barely able to keep her eyes open. He held her hands and made an attempt to comfort her. Devammaji whispered, 'Mahaswami, I feel extremely weak and tired. Please take care of my little rajkumari. I want her named Gowru.' Gowramma was the name of Devammaji's maternal grandmother, whom she had loved and admired. In the flickering light of the oil lamp, he saw her eyes roll; a moment later, her fingers went limp and slipped from his hands.

His other wife, Subadhramma, was in the throes of labour in the next bed. Veerarajendra stood beside Devammaji's bed in deep distress. In spite of the pain she was in, Subadhramma assured her husband, 'Mahaswami, Devammaji was like my elder sister. I will take care of her baby Gowru. I will raise her along with my child.' Subadhramma's words were of some consolation to Veerarajendra as he looked at the newborn lying next to her lifeless mother.

At the crack of dawn the following day, as the sun rose above the great river, Subadhramma's child arrived. The holy city, as usual, woke to the sounds of temple bells and conch shells. Subadhramma named her child after the sacred river and called her Gangamma. The joy of arrival of two new lives in the royal household was marred by the tragedy of performing the last rites of Devammaji at the Lingayat jangamvadi on the banks of river Ganges. Veerarajendra needed the permission of the British to leave Coorg Nest. Captain Carpenter was present whenever the raja ventured outside his haveli, which was not too often.

True to her word, Subadhramma nursed Gowru along with her little Ganga, and felt like a mother of twins. Veerarajendra visited her everyday to enquire about the two rajkumaris, especially Gowru. Gowramma was his first daughter born to one of his three royal consorts. The loss of Devammaji shattered him and he was overtly protective of his little motherless daughter. Under Subadhramma's impartial care, both the babies thrived. When the girls were a little older than six months, Veerarajendra carried Gowru for the first time. In his arms, the girl cooed and gurgled. Her toothless smile was most endearing and her large dark brown eyes were full of delight. When the maidservant came to take her back, she resisted and clung to her father. Gowramma soon won Veerarajendra's heart and became his favourite child. He affectionately called her his *kombakki*, the imperial pigeon that abounded in his erstwhile kingdom.

Of his six sons and three daughters at the time, he deliberately kept aloof from the boys, mainly from remorse that he had deprived them the legacy of a dynasty started by his ancestor,

Haleri Veeraraja, seven generations earlier. This deep sense of guilt strained his relationship with his sons. He dreaded the thought of them questioning him about their forefathers. His eldest son, Chitrashekara, born to one of his minor wives, was now nine years old and already inquisitive. All his sons were timid in his overbearing presence, and this made Veerarajendra loathe them even more.

Eight months had passed since the death of Devammaji, and the birth of his two favourite daughters. Gowru and Ganga were the only two children with whom he played and found happiness in their growth. Both the girls had started to take tentative steps and were everyday adding new sounds to their vocabulary. Gowru would cling to her father's legs and refuse to leave when Subadhramma and the maidservants came to take the two girls back to their room.

The days rolled by. It was the beginning of summer and the festival of *holi* was being celebrated with great fervour in Benares. People smeared coloured rice flour on each other, and there was a great deal of gaiety everywhere. The air was heavy with the fragrance of ripe mangoes from the mango orchard in front of the raja's haveli. For the first time, Veerarajendra felt the longing to celebrate holi with his family. His children frolicked happily in the compound, splashing colours on one another. Veerarajendra had eyes only for Gowru and Ganga, who were happily splashing in the coloured water specially kept for them in shallow pails.

The rare moment of celebration at Coorg Nest was suddenly interrupted by the sound of raised voices. A man clad in saffron robes had appeared at the gate, demanding to meet the raja. The guards did not allow him to enter, as they had been instructed by Captain Carpenter not to permit any visitors without his permission. Curious to see the visitor, Veerarajendra went to investigate and immediately recognised Alamanda Somayya, whose family had been known to the Haleri rajas for several generations. At once, Veerarajendra sent a servant to seek Captain Carpenter's permission to receive his guest. Veerarajendra knew Somayya from his childhood days, and was keen to receive news of his erstwhile kingdom. In the last eight years, he had some visitors, but the British allowed only a select few to meet the raja. Days earlier, Captain Carpenter had discussed with his superior, Major W.M. Stewart, about relaxing the restrictions on Veerarajendra in light of his satisfactory conduct, and absence of any anti-British activities since his arrival at Benares.

Captain Carpenter, who lived nearby, was in a relaxed mood that day, and gave permission for the visitor to have a chat with the raja. Somayya respectfully touched Veerarajendra's feet and said that he had come to the holy city to visit all the temples and to take a dip in the sacred river Ganges. He bowed and said: 'Mahaswami, I also wanted to meet you and enquire about your welfare.' He was happy to see the raja enjoying holi with his children. As soon as Somayya sauntered into the compound, all the women covered their faces and scurried indoors.

Somayya was a head taller than Veerarajendra and possessed an imposing personality. He surveyed the premises and shook his head in disbelief at the predicament of the beleaguered Veerarajendra. He was about the same age as the raja. Somayya had seen the pomp and splendour of Veerarajendra's life at his two palaces in Kodagu. Veerarajendra was eager to hear the latest news from his former kingdom. He anxiously asked Somayya: 'Do people miss me? Do they talk about me? Are they happy under the rule of the foreigners?' He enquired further, 'Is it true churches have been built where once temples stood? Is the Omkareshwara temple still there? Are they converting people to Christianity?'

What Somayya had to say did not please Veerarajendra. Somayya explained how in the eight years since the raja had been dethroned, the life of the common man had vastly improved. Several schools had been opened and education was available for both boys and girls. People felt safe, were free to cultivate their land, and practise their religion and rituals without hindrance. 'Yes, there are new churches. The temple in the fort was dismantled after the British established their headquarters there. In its place, a chapel has been built. But they have not disturbed any other places of worship,' he said. He confirmed that the British were making subtle attempts at conversion but were cautious not to upset the sentiments of the people.

Veerarajendra listened intently to Somayya as the latter narrated the incident of the revolt against the Britishs three years after they took over his kingdom. However, it was not a popular uprising. Most of the Kodavas sided with the British in putting down the rebels who were led by a man proclaiming to be a descendent of the Haleri dynasty. Somayya's admission that he too had sided with the East India Company to quell the rebellion shocked Veerarajendra. The British had rewarded those who supported them handsomely. Somayya was the recipient of a special silver medallion, gold coins, livestock, guns and land from the British.

'New roads are being laid. A bridge across river Kavery near Siddapur has greatly improved travel between north and south of the province. There are many more bridges under construction,' he further added.

Veerarajendra abused the feringhees when he heard that his palace had been converted into a *kacheri* or headquarters from where the British officers administered Kodagu. Somayya's comments dashed any hopes that Veerarajendra still entertained of returning to his land. He felt wretched when Somayya praised neighbouring Mysore where the royal family continued to rule their land peacefully as a protectorate of the British East India Company. 'If only you had listened to wiser counsel, instead of that former kennel-keeper Kunta Basava whom you elevated to the position of Dewan, you would not have landed yourself and your family in this quagmire,' pointed out Somayya.

Veerarajendra reacted angrily, 'I was not going to be a slave of the white man. The British betrayed me and my forefathers, despite our family's help to them in vanquishing Hyder Ali and his son Tipu Sultan.' He lamented, 'In the end, it is the pusillanimous Wodeyars of Mysore who benefited.'

Somayya and Veerarajendra talked well into the evening. Somayya told the raja that he was on a pilgrimage to all the holy sites in north India, which would take him about three years to complete. He wanted to learn about the Hindu religion from the *rishis* or sages. Only after completing his spiritual journey would he return to Kodagu and start a family. Veerarajendra was shocked when he heard Somayya say, 'If I do not get satisfactory answers to my spiritual queries, I might even consider embracing Christianity.'

'That means you will commit the most heinous crime of eating the flesh of the sacred cow?' Veerarajendra reprimanded him.

Somayya was quick to reply: 'No Mahaswami, I will never do that, and the British have given strict instructions not to permit cow-slaughter in Kodagu.' Lieutenant Colonel Mark Cubbon, the chief commissioner since 1836, had taken care not to offend the people of Kodagu in any way. With his assurances and actions, he had endeared himself to the general populace. Somayya informed the raja that Colonel Fraser, having been promoted to major general, was now posted as the commissioner of Mysore.

Veerarajendra berated Fraser and said, 'The feringhees are cunning and deceitful. I do not trust them.'

The talk then turned to personal matters. Somayya was pained to hear about the untimely passing away of Devammaji who was distantly related to him. He requested to see Devammaji's daughter. When little Gowramma was brought to him, he was very much impressed by the child. Gowramma still had remnants of some of the colours of holi on her face. He studied her tiny palms and said: 'I see lines that indicate this Rajkumari will one day cross the seas.'

Veerarajendra laughed and said: 'Impossible! I am not letting her out of my sight.'

Somayya took out a small silver container from his pocket and scooped out a little of the sandalwood paste. With his middle finger he applied the paste on Gowramma's forehead and blessed her: 'May Lord Kasi Viswanath protect you, and keep you safe.'

Dusk descended on the holy city, but the two old friends were unaware of the passing time till a guard came in to remind the raja that it was time for the visitor to depart. Somayya stood up to take leave of Veerarajendra, and promised to see him on his way back to Kodagu after completing his pilgrimage. He had plans to visit the shrines at Kedarnath and Badrinath too. Somayya added, 'I hope to see you again Mahaswami, if I am alive, and not fallen victim to the thugs who strangle wayfarers in the name of goddess Kali.'

Veerarajendra could not sleep that night; he tossed and turned in bed, recalling his conversation with Somayya. The unpalatable truth was that the British had won the loyalty of his subjects. He sadly realised that his hopes of ever returning to his kingdom were almost non-existent. He was condemned to spend the rest of his life in Benares, as a virtual prisoner of the white man.

During the last three months, Munshi Shantamalla, a Brahmin from Kodagu who had accompanied the raja, was reading to him the *Rajendraname*—a chronicle of the history of the Haleri dynasty complied by his uncle Dodda Veerarajendra. Veerarajendra had faint recollections of his father Lingarajendra narrating the history of his ancestors. Now, when he heard it in detail from Shantamalla, his heart sank. He had lost a dynasty that his forefathers had carefully nurtured over two centuries. It was ironic that around the year 1600 when his ancestor Veeraraja had founded the Haleri dynasty, a trading entity named the British East India Company was constituted in London, which now ruled his fate.

The British became involved in the affairs of Kodagu during the period when Hyder Ali and Tipu Sultan started becoming powerful in the south and posed a threat to the Company's security and trade. Veerarajendra's uncle, Dodda Veerarajendra, had entered into a treaty with the British East India Company to fight their common enemy. His father Lingarajendra continued to maintain good relationships with the white man.

Veerarajendra agonised with hindsight that perhaps diplomacy with the British would have served him better. He too could have been like the Wodeyars of Mysore. He fell into deep slumber just before dawn. Later, he heard distant sound of drums and trumpets. He woke up with a start to find himself covered in cold sweat. He realised that he had been having a nightmare—he was on an elephant riding out of the Mercara fort. The palace band was playing 'The British Grenadier'. In the dream, his subjects were dancing and laughing at him.

A few weeks later, there were three more guests from Kodagu. They were cousins of his rani, Kongettira Kaveramma. Veerarajendra was not keen on meeting the visitors after what he had heard from Alamanda Somayya, and his horrible recurring nightmare. He dreaded hearing again that in barely eight years he had become irrelevant in his erstwhile realm. His subjects had not pardoned him for his tyrannical rule. The three visitors met Kaveramma, who was woefully homesick. He felt bleak and forlorn dwelling on all the depressing memories. It was only in the presence of his two daughters, Gowru and Ganga, that he found some comfort.

2

VEERARAJENDRA GETS A HELPING HAND

EVER SINCE HIS arrival at Benares, a matter had kept nagging Veerarajendra. In fact, he had raised the issue with Colonel James S. Fraser days before he was exiled from his kingdom. It was about two promissory notes on deposits of 2,03,900 sicca* rupees at four percent interest, and another 6,53,940 Madras rupees at six percent interest that his uncle Dodda Veerarajendra had invested with the British East India Company in the name of his daughter and heir, Devammaji (not to be mistaken with Veerarajendra's wife of

*The rupee in different provinces in India had varying values until the British standardised the currency in 1835 throughout their colony. The exchange value of rupee was pegged at ten rupees to one pound sterling.

the same name). The British had promised Dodda Veerarajendra that they would be guardians to his young daughters after his death. Devammaji sat on the throne of Kodagu as a nine-year-old queen after her father's demise in 1809. However, within a year, her uncle Lingarajendra had cunningly usurped the throne. He placated the British officers and tactfully convinced the Company to pay him the interest earned on the deposits so that he could take care of Devammaji and her three sisters.

The Company continued to pay the interest to Lingarajendra's son, Veerarajendra, after he ascended the throne in 1820. About twelve years later, the British got reports of the raja and his infamous Dewan, Kunta Basava, having connived in brutally murdering Devammaji and two of her sisters. Since the funds were for the welfare of Devammaji and her sisters, the British stopped payment of interest on these investments from 1833 onwards.

Colonel Fraser had informed the raja, 'The proceeds of the deposit can be paid only to the legal heirs of Dodda Veerarajendra.'

'I am the sole surviving heir of my uncle. You have already appropriated sixteen lakh rupees from my treasury,' the deposed raja argued with the colonel.

The British agent justified the action by saying, 'What's in the treasury belongs to the people of the land, and will be used for their benefit. Moreover, we have reliable intelligence to prove it was on your instructions that your men murdered Rani Devammaji.' Veerarajendra had tried in vain to convince the British officer that his cousin Devammaji and her sisters had died of cholera. Finally, Colonel Fraser had put an end to the debate by telling Veerarajendra, 'The only person who can decide this issue is Governor-General Lord William Bentinck in Calcutta.'

In 1842, Veerarajendra petitioned Governor-General Lord Ellenborough for refund of the deposit, which he once again claimed rightfully belonging to him. The deposit with accumulated interest since 1833 would be more than 12,00,000 rupees, according to his assistant, Munshi Shantamalla's calculations. However, the raja's attempts proved futile. He pursued the matter with Lord Ellenborough's successor, Lord Henry Hardinge. However, the British East India Company refused to recognise him as the legal heir of his uncle Dodda Veerarajendra, and continued to ignore his appeals. The British stuck to their assertion that the daughters of Dodda Veerarajendra had died of unnatural causes, and blamed the junior Veerarajendra for their demise. Moreover, they insisted that the deposits belonged to the state of Coorg, where the administration had been taken over by the Company as a sovereign power. Nevertheless, Veerarajendra fantasised about what he could achieve with that amount of money at his disposal; he would be able to buy favours, even from the British. Just getting the principal amount would make a substantial difference to him and his family.

A favour bestowed by the raja on a British doctor named William Jeaffreson during his rule, came as an unexpected ray of hope. Way back in 1830, the then twenty-eight-year-old Veerarajendra had been suddenly taken seriously ill. The native doctors were of the opinion that he required surgery. A worried Veerarajendra requested his friend and ally the British Resident, Arthur Cole at Mysore, to depute a British surgeon to examine him. Unable to send a doctor from any of the nearby cantonments, Arthur Cole requested his counterpart at Bombay to despatch a surgeon to Coorg immediately.

Dr Jeaffreson, who had recently arrived in India, was asked to travel to Coorg to treat Veerarajendra. Accordingly, Dr Jeaffreson set out for Coorg accompanied by Captain Hill, an army officer. By the time they reached Coorg, the raja's illness had somehow mysteriously disappeared; Veerarajendra had fully recovered from his ailment and was now in good health. The raja invited the affable doctor and the officer to spend a few days in his palace at Madikeri. The relationship between the raja of Coorg and the British was cordial at the time. During the course of their conversation, Dr Jeaffreson and Captain Hill spoke about their interest in hunting. Veerarajendra was spontaneous in arranging a grand *shikar* in his kingdom for his two guests. Hunting big game in the thick forests of Kodagu was a passion that the raja and his ancestors had pursued with great zeal.

Dr Jeaffreson and Captain Hill stayed on in Coorg for the next twenty-two days, hunting big game found in such abundance that they never had imagined in their wildest dreams. Accompanied by the hospitable raja, they spent several days in the dense jungle, hunting elephants, tigers, spotted deer, wild boars, jungle fowl, and many other wild game. A team of cooks prepared delicious dishes of bush-meat while they camped in the forest. They were astounded that the raja had mobilised nearly five-thousand of his men to clear the jungle in order to help them in the hunting. Each expedition lasted about three to four days, with interludes for entertainment at the palace. Veerarajendra took great pride in showing his visitors his extraordinary collection of guns and armaments used for hunting.

Between Dr Jeaffreson and Captain Hill, they had shot half a dozen tigers, a few mammoth-sized elephants, and several other game. By the end of their stay, they had an impressive collection of deerskin, tiger pelts, claws, ivory and mounted trophies. Dr Jeaffreson was highly indebted to the raja for the unforgettable hospitality that he and his companion had enjoyed. Veerarajendra had a well-trained band in the palace that played many Western tunes surprisingly well. They played 'God save the King' as Dr Jeaffreson and Captain Hill took leave of the raja, after their sojourn in Coorg. Dr Jeaffreson was deeply touched at the raja's hospitality and offered his services to the raja anytime it was required.

However, by 1832, the relationship between Veerarajendra and the East India Company had started to deteriorate. Veerarajendra had provoked the East India Company by his defiant actions. There were many reports of atrocities instigated by the raja on the family members of his uncle, Dodda Veerarajendra. The common citizens too suffered under the increasingly despotic rule of the raja and his cohorts. To avoid persecution, his sister and brother-in-law had sought refuge under the British in Mysore. The British found this an ideal opportunity to deepen their involvement in the affairs of Coorg.

In December 1832, fearing retaliation from the British, Veerarajendra sent a message to his friend Dr Jeaffreson in Bombay, to influence the British East India Company's officers in Madras and Bombay.

Veerarajendra's letter to Dr Jeaffreson, translated, read as follows:

In the year 1830, you favoured me with a visit, and remained with me for twenty-two days—an interval of time, which afforded you a sufficient opportunity for observing my private character, as well as the system adopted by me in the government of my dominions.

I now regret to inform you, that a misunderstanding has lately arisen between Mr Casamajor, Resident of Mysore, and myself, the occasion of which was as follows:

One Chen Buswah, a married man [to a sister of the raja], and, in addition to having had a free grant of land from me, had received many proofs of my royal favour and kindness. This person, without any provocation whatsoever, and solely instigated by his own evil passions, collected together a number of armed followers, and placing himself at their head, raised the standard of revolt, for the purpose of dethroning me.

His attempts, however, proving unsuccessful; Chen Buswah fled, and escaped to the British frontier, having previously to his so doing, cruelly tortured, and afterwards poisoned a person who had offended him, besides having, during his fight, killed two men, and severely wounded one, who had endeavoured to intercept him.

This atrocious criminal, I am sorry to say, received protection from Mr Casamajor, the British Resident at Mysore: a circumstance the more extraordinary, since, from the time that the friendship and alliance between British Government and my ancestors first took place, we have been blended together like sugar and milk, or as you would express it—we have been hand-and-glove together; in short, almost one and the same state.

The extradition of criminals was, in fact, a constant and invariable rule between us, and had, as is well known to every British officer, been established for a very long time. Acting, therefore, in perfect conformity therewith, I repeatedly wrote to Mr Casamajor, requiring him to deliver up to me the said criminal; but although in addition to so doing, I thrice sent persons duly authorized to demand and receive him, they as often returned empty-handed. I am sorry to say that Mr Casamajor still persists in his conduct, not even deigning to reply to my requisitions.

I assure you dear sir, that the pain and mortification occasioned me by this circumstance have been very great, especially as I am, and always intend to be, the staunch and faithful ally of the British Government. But it must be evident to you, that the infringement of the above regulation will, by lessening the respect of my subjects for me, cause disaffection among them, and thus undermine the very foundation of my authority.

I cannot express the regret I feel at having to trouble a British officer with my grievances, but how am I to maintain my character as an independent prince if my legitimate authority be thus wrested from me?

Having, however, whenever called upon, cheerfully come forward to assist the British Government with aid and reinforcement, I trust that I shall be treated by them in the manner such services merit.

In conclusion, I beg of you, my dear sir, to advise me what I had best do in this matter. It is my sincere wish, I assure you, to still observe all the terms of the alliance with your Government as religiously as I have hitherto done; and all I ask for, in return, is a reciprocal observance of the same upon their part, and the consequent delivering up to me of Chen Bushwah and his adherents.

I entreat to you, therefore, to use your influence in amicably arranging this untoward circumstance, and by doing so you will, at one and the same time, relieve me from great anxiety, and ensure my lasting esteem and gratitude.

And now, what more can I say, than to desire you to consider me as your friend, and that you will continue to favour me, from time to time, with accounts of your health and welfare.

Veer Rajunder Wadeer

Dr William Jeaffreson promptly sent a reply on 12 January 1833 through a bearer in response to Veerarajendra's appeal:

Honourable and Dear Sir,

I have been favoured with your letter, and hasten to answer it, and sympathize with your Highness on the distress which the circumstances detailed in it must have occasioned, and which demands immediate justice to render your future reign glorious, secure, and happy, and which justice your treaty with the English nation entitles you to exact. I must however, hope and believe that there has been some misunderstanding, or want of proper explanation, withheld from the Resident of Mysore, or justice would have been dealt out to you, and the murderers who have taken shelter under his jurisdiction given up on a regular and formal request being made; for this is doubtless the first law of treaty between all nations, and one that the English always hold the most sacred and inviolable. It will afford me much satisfaction to render your Highness any aid, and accordingly, I beg to introduce the bearer of this, by name Mohammed Ghyeasoodden Mooftee, a gentleman well acquainted with native law as well as English manners and customs, and native courts. He will confer with your Highness, and point out the most easy way to gain redress for your past wrongs, as well as to prevent a recurrence of them in future. My friend will obey your instructions, and will communicate your Highness's pleasure to me. In the meantime, I beg to assure your Highness that I shall ever remain,

Your sincere friend and well-wisher,

W. Jeaffreson

The doctor had strongly defended the raja of Coorg as a decent man and a good friend of the British. Both he and Captain Hill tried their best to impress upon the British officers not to take any drastic actions against the raja. In Dr Jeaffreson's opinion, the British East India Company had wrongly vilified Veerarajendra, and the allegations against him were false. He had witnessed the proceedings at the raja's court, and had found him to be fair and kind to his subjects, who in turn loved their sovereign.

However, Dr Jeaffreson did not succeed in his attempts to help Veerarajendra from being overthrown by the East India Company. He was also warned by the Resident at Bombay not to interfere in the political affairs of the Company. Already Veerarajendra had made matters irretrievably worse for himself by taking the East India Company's native emissary Kullapally Karunakara Menon as hostage, and refusing to release him.

So, when Jeaffreson heard of Veerarajendra's exile and the annexation of Coorg, he was deeply upset. He felt that the British East India Company had been rapacious, and had not only cheated the raja but also deprived him of his kingdom and wealth. The rajas of Coorg were traditional allies of the British, and the doctor was dismayed at the Company for letting down a good friend.

Soon after, Dr Jeaffreson returned to England, and after spending a few years in other postings, returned to India. Around 1847, he paid a visit to Veerarajendra at Benares. He was profoundly saddened to see the former king of Kodagu living in a haveli which was crowded with his growing family and entourage. He recalled with nostalgia the wonderful time he and Captain Hill had spent in the raja's erstwhile kingdom. At the time of his visit to Benares, Gowru and Ganga were six-year-olds and the only two children of the raja to be running around freely in his presence. Subadhramma, a good singer, had taught the entire brood of the raja a few songs and prayers. Jeaffreson was much pleased when Ganga and Gowru sang for him some of the ballads popular in Coorg households.

Veerarajendra told Jeaffreson that all his children were being trained to enact stories from the Indian epics—the *Ramayana* and the *Mahabharata*. He promised to stage a performance by his children for the doctor during his next visit to Coorg Nest.

However, it was apparent to Dr Jeaffreson that only Gowru and Ganga were the favourites of the raja, and that the other children were kept at a distance. The raja referred to Gowramma as a 'pigeon among crows' and the 'fairest of the flock'. Dr Jeaffreson was pleased to find little Gowramma learning to speak English from Mrs Carpenter on the raja's request. Mrs Carpenter would also often narrate stories from the Bible to the six-year-old princess.

Captain Carpenter (promoted to Lt Colonel by then), having watched over Veerarajendra for fourteen years since 1834, thought it safe to give permission for Dr Jeaffreson to visit the raja at regular intervals. The raja and his doctor friend would often reminisce about their hunting experiences in Coorg nearly two decades ago. During one of their meetings, Veerarajendra brought up the issue of the twelve lakh rupees in investments and accumulated interest left in safe custody of the British East India Company, by his uncle Dodda Veerarajendra. He sought Dr Jeaffreson's help and advice to recover the amount. After several days of contemplation and consultations with legal experts, Dr Jeaffreson came up with an idea. He advised the raja to file a legal suit at the London Chancery Court against the British East India Company for the recovery of the two investments.

Veerarajendra was at a loss as to how such a brazen idea could be implemented. Astonished, he enquired: 'Jeaffresonji, please explain how can I file a legal suit against the Company sitting here in Benares?'

Jeaffreson did not have an immediate answer. He toyed with the idea of going to London and filing the suit on behalf of the raja. Jeaffreson replied, 'Mahaswami, please give me a few days to think this over.' Veerarajendra offered to pay Dr Jeaffreson a retainer for him to work out a scheme to recover the deposit amount along with the accrued interest.

These discussions with Jeaffreson lifted the sagging morale of Veerarajendra. He eagerly awaited his well-wisher's visits and further proposals. Jeaffreson had friends who had contacts with the newly appointed governor-general—the thirty-five-year-old Lord Dalhousie. He had further consultations with legal experts on the modalities of filing a suit by a dethroned Indian ruler against the Company—a unique step indeed. No deposed royalty had ever tried the British legal system at home to recover their wealth appropriated by the British East India Company. Jeaffreson gathered sufficient information to conclude that the raja had a good case to file a legal suit at the Chancery Court against the Company.

However, Jeaffreson realised there was one major hurdle—the raja would need to be personally present in London to file a case against the Company. Until then, no Indian royalty had ever visited Britain. If Veerarajendra's intention was known, Lord Dalhousie would certainly never give permission for the raja of Coorg to visit London and embarrass the East India Company with a legal suit.

In the United Kingdom, it was the time of the industrial revolution and a period of significant social, economic and technological progresses. The young Princess Alexandrina Victoria had been catapulted to the throne of Britain in 1837. She had turned just eighteen at the time, and Queen Victoria was the titular head of the country that ruled the seas and had colonies in far-flung lands of the earth. Unprecedented events were taking place in the western world. Britain was already a parliamentary democracy. The influence of the monarchy was mainly ceremonial, and the industrial revolution was rapidly changing the standard of living. Queen Victoria grew in stature over the years. She, along with her prince consort, Prince Albert, played an important role in guiding the administration, though the decision of the parliament was supreme. With a growing educated middle class, and the influence of the Fourth Estate, some of the liberals had begun to question the exploitation of the people in the colonies. The once flourishing slave trade had been abolished since 1801, and the British were actively involved in preventing its practice in other parts of the world. Dr Jeaffreson realised that it was the ideal time for him to initiate the process of filing a legal suit by Veerarajendra against the East India Company. Judging from the mood of the people, he anticipated support in the parliament, the press, and from the public. He was, however, in a dilemma as to how to get permission from the truculent Governor-General Lord Dalhousie for the raja to travel to London.

After a few days of contemplation, Dr Jeaffreson concluded that Veerarajendra should formally request the governor-general for permission to visit England so that the process could be set in motion. He then devised an ingenious idea. Impressed at having seen little Gowramma speak a smattering of English, and the tutoring she was receiving about the Bible, the doctor advised the raja to write to Lord Dalhousie stating he desired to visit England to enable his daughter receive a Christian education. Dr Jeaffreson was sure such a reason would certainly appeal to the Governor-General and the Court of Directors of the Company. He drafted a skillfully worded letter on behalf of the raja to Lord Dalhousie, which Veerarajendra signed and dispatched on 2 March 1848:

My Lord,

I desire to address your Lordship on a subject, which is near my heart, although I feel it an impropriety on my part to enter into a detail of family matters.

My manner of life, by the blessings of God, and as man can testify, for the last fourteen years that I have been under the care and keeping of Government, has been without reproach. Colonel Carpenter knows this, he having been uniformly with me since I left my country; and, besides this several gentlemen holding high offices at this place can give their testimony.

When I resided in my own country, I had a predilection for European customs; subsequently to my residence in this province, this impression has been confirmed; and, adverting to the principles of the Christian religion as taught by its Founder, it has become my anxious wish that my daughter should receive a Christian education in England.

But in this design I can receive no aid from those with whom I have affinity; and, situated as I am here, I am unable to effect it. My daughter has, for some time past, adopted English habits and manners. This is known to Colonel Carpenter and other officers at this station, who can testify to it, if necessary.

I am anxious that she should proceed to England, to be brought up at such a place and in such a manner as the daughter of an English nobleman would receive her education.

If Her Gracious Majesty, Queen Victoria, should extend her favour also to my daughter, my happiness would be complete.

I trust the British Government will not object to my daughter, through your lordships' gracious interposition, proceeding to England, suitably to her rank and condition. The love of a parent to his child is obvious. I place my confidence in your lordship's kindness, and state my request exactly as I wish. I am the first of the native chiefs, your lordship will observe, who has made this proposition. My daughter's age is six years and six months; and at this tender age, the good effects of education are more certain than at a later period. It is not a great matter for your lordship to assent to my request. We look to you for indulgent consideration. Believe me to be sincere in my well wishes, and to be anxious for an early intimation of assent to my request.

I remain, etc.,

Veer Rajunder Wadeer
Rajah of Coorg

The letter served its purpose—Dalhousie's interest was roused. He obtained detailed reports of Veerarajendra and his family from Colonel Carpenter and Major Stewart. During one of his visits to Benares, he asked to meet the young princess. He, however, did not want the father to be present. Accordingly, Mrs Carpenter brought Gowramma and her half-sister Gangamma to the government house where Lord Dalhousie was camping. The governor-general found Gowramma to be an attractive and intelligent child. He was happy to see that Gowramma could already converse in English, though hesitatingly. However, the striking oriental beauty of Gangamma caught his eye. He regretted that the raja of Coorg had decided that his better-looking daughter was to remain a heathen.

Nonetheless, Lord Dalhousie, known for his contempt for Indian rajas, maharajas, sultans and badshahs, was in no hurry to respond to Veerarajendra's letter.

3

MAHARAJA DULEEP SINGH

$\mathcal{I}$T WAS THE summer of 1849. While on a visit to Calcutta, Dr Jeaffreson learnt from his British acquaintances that his friend and colleague Dr John Login had been appointed the guardian of the eleven-year-old Maharaja Duleep Singh, the son and successor of Maharaja Ranjit Singh. Soon after the death of the powerful Ranjit Singh ten years earlier, the British had started meddling in the affairs of the North-West Frontier. The internecine war within the palace had eliminated all the legitimate sons of Ranjit Singh except the youngest—Duleep Singh. On 18 September 1843, at the age of five, Duleep Singh ascended the throne of Punjab. His mother, Maharani Jindan Kaur, as the Regent, was the real power behind the throne. However, using clever manoeuvres and discarding earlier treaties, Governor-General Dalhousie annexed this last major bastion of the Indians and brought it under the rule of the East India Company in 1849.

Dr John Spencer Login was a highly influential doctor, who, apart from practising medicine, undertook several assignments from the Company. He had spent many years in Punjab and the North-West Frontier. He had been the resident doctor at Lucknow before his posting in Punjab. Compassionate and deeply religious, Dr Login endeared himself to the rich as well as the poor. He soon became a confidante of Governor-General Dalhousie and the influential Lawrence brothers—Sir Henry and John. Both Lord Dalhousie and Sir Henry Lawrence were godparents to the Logins' children.

Sir Henry Lawrence, the Resident at Lahore, was responsible for appointing his close associate and friend, Dr Login, as the commander of Maharaja Ranjit Singh's citadel at Lahore. The doctor was entrusted with the guardianship of Maharaja Duleep Singh, the minor son and successor of the 'Lion of Punjab'. Prior to this assignment, Dr Login and his wife Lena were posted in Lucknow and had forged a close friendship with the royal family of Oudh. He had also served as the Postmaster General of the kingdom.

Dr Login was in great demand by the families of the nawabs, rajas and zamindars. When Dr Login went to the local palaces to treat the women there, his wife often accompanied him. Lena Login could converse in the local language, and made friends with the women in the zenanas. Even though a doctor, John Login was not allowed to see the women directly, as they were in purdah. Women patients would stand behind a screen and put a hand or stick their tongue through a hole in the partition for the doctor to inspect. Grateful patients sent deeply unsuitable gifts, which the Logins had to exercise great tact in refusing. Two baby elephants attended by Siddhi (of African origin) slaves were once delivered at their residence. Large hunting-cats were also sent on another occasion, as playmates for their two young sons. Politely returning these gifts must have strained even Mrs Login's diplomatic skills. Lena Login was one of the few British women to experience and gather intimate knowledge of life in the zenanas of the royalty in north India of that period. The begums were her close friends, and were in turn curious to know from her the customs and lifestyle of the European memsahibs.

The following week Dr Jeaffreson hurried to Coorg Nest, anxious to give Veerarajendra the news of the latest development. He was excited as he told the raja, 'I think I have found just the person who could help us in the case.' He told the raja about Dr John Login and his wife, Lena Login. 'Both the doctor and his wife Lena are well known in high circles of the British administration as well as the Indian royal families. I have not met the doctor for more than a decade. I am told his wife Lena Campbell, who is from Scotland, is a lively woman liked both by the British and the natives.'

Veerarajendra said: 'You have brought good news, Jeaffresonji. Please tell me what else I should do to obtain permission from the Company to visit London.' It was dusk, and from one corner of the haveli, Jeaffreson heard the children and the women chorus their evening prayer.

'Yes, Mahaswami, I am sure the Almighty will soon shower his grace on you and your family. I am planning a trip to Delhi and will go over to Lahore to meet my friend Dr John Login. I will be able to give you more details on my return.'

On hearing about Maharaja Ranjit Singh, Veerarajendra was reminded of an outlandish scheme once suggested to him by his favourite dewan, Kunta Basava, and the evil genius in his court, Abbas Ali. The bizarre proposal was that the raja of Coorg should seek the help of the 'Lion of Punjab' to stave off the invasion by the British during the summer of 1834. A Sikh named Lahore Singh was travelling through South India at that time, and had visited Veerarajendra's court in Coorg. He had mentioned the powerful Sikh maharaja, and how even the British were fearful of the 'Lion of Punjab' and did not dare attack his territories. Dewan Kunta Basava, an illiterate, was as ignorant as Veerarajendra of the distance between Coorg and Punjab!

Dr Jeaffreson explained to Veerarajendra how after the demise of Ranjit Singh, the British East India Company had created internal dissention and usurped control of this large and prosperous region of India. The naïve Maharaja Duleep Singh was quite oblivious of the contents of the Byrowal Treaty, which he had signed when he was barely nine years old. Under this devious pact, the British took over guardianship of the young maharaja, and formed a Council of Regents to govern Punjab. Maharani Jindan Kaur and the Sikh leaders accepted the Byrowal Treaty as it was assured that Duleep Singh would be the sovereign ruler of Punjab as soon as he attained the age of sixteen.

By the time Dr Jeaffreson finally reached Lahore, the capital of Punjab, and established contact with Dr John Login, it was November 1849. Dr Login's wife, Lena, was away in England along with her three young children for health reasons. Duleep Singh's mother, Maharani Jindan Kaur, a strong-willed personality, was kept under detention by the British and isolated from her son. In the absence of parental guidance and affection, the young maharaja soon forged a strong bond with the kindly doctor. Dr Login provided the emotional support of a doting parent to the young boy, which prompted the innocent Duleep Singh to refer to the doctor as his 'Ma-Bap'. The British also began the subtle indoctrination of the eleven-year-old Duleep Singh to make him turn away from his own mother.

After a British-instigated Second Sikh War, Lord Dalhousie annexed Punjab, disregarding the Byrowal Treaty, and made the child maharaja sign in March 1849 the terms of settlement, known as the Lahore Treaty, whereby he renounced 'for himself, his heirs and his successors, all right, title and claim to the sovereignty of Punjab.' By subsequent clauses of the same agreement 'all property of Punjab, of whatever description and wheresoever found were confiscated to the East India Company. The famed Koh-i-noor diamond was surrendered to Queen Victoria of England.' A pension of not less than four and not exceeding five lakhs of rupees was allotted for the maharaja for the support of himself, his relatives, and the servants of the state. However, this amount would be payable only after Duleep Singh attained the age of sixteen. His guardian, Dr Login, was paid an annual allowance of 1,000-pound sterling (equivalent to 10,000 rupees at that time). Duleep Singh was permitted by Dalhousie the dubious distinction of retaining the title of 'maharaja'. The British Resident at Lahore, Sir Henry Lawrence, was however not in favour of the deceitful measures adopted by the Governor-General. He expressed strong displeasure at the blatant disregard of the Byrowal Treaty. However, Lord Dalhousie overruled these objections and justified use of any means to achieve his goal of seizing total control of India.

During Dr Jeaffreson's sojourn in Lahore, Governor-General Lord Dalhousie arrived on a state visit to the capital of Punjab.

Sir Henry Lawrence threw a grand party in honour of the Governor-General, to which the eleven-year-old Maharaja Duleep Singh too was invited. Duleep Singh made a grand entrance, seated in the exquisite silver howdah on his elephant. Dr Login took Dr Jeaffreson along as his guest to the party where there were other high-ranking officers of the East India Company, including the controversial commander-in-chief of the army, Sir Charles Napier who had recently conquered the province of Sindh. Another important official was John Lawrence (appointed Viceroy a few years later), the authoritative younger brother of Sir Henry Lawrence. Dr Jeaffreson was introduced to Lord Dalhousie and had a lengthy conversation with the Governor-General. He found the young Governor-General bigoted and highly patronising of the locals. In the annexation of Punjab, the British East India Company had surpassed itself in the art of duplicity and deception. The childish maharaja was placated with toys, picture books and painting sets after making him sign away his entire kingdom and all his wealth.

Dr Jeaffreson felt guilty that his fellow citizens were indulging in such dishonest acts of betrayal, cunning and deceit. At the same time, he saw better administration and equitable laws being introduced in India, which enabled the common man to lead a more peaceful life. Dalhousie justified his actions and emphasised his firm belief that the people of India would benefit from British rule.

Lord Dalhousie had elaborate plans for investments in education, highways, railways, telegraph and irrigation canals in the subcontinent. He had gained vast experience in these developmental works when he assisted the British parliamentarian, and later prime minister, William Ewart Gladstone. Dalhousie had served a five-year term as one of the youngest member of the British Parliament. He had demonstrated his administrative abilities as the president of the Board of Trade. When he was bestowed the coveted post of Governor-General of India, he was full of ambitious ideas, and impatient to improve the facilities in the vast colony. Though young and blessed with a sharp mind, Dalhousie was not of robust health. In his quest for introducing modern communication and transport systems in India, he was intolerant of any impediments and often high-handed. He was determined to provide Britain with cheap labour and access to the immense resources abundantly available in India.

Dr Jeaffreson listened to Dalhousie, the Lawrence brothers and Sir Napier discuss about the polytheistic Indian people and their rulers, and how it was the 'chosen duty of the British' to show the Indians the route to salvation by introducing them to the words of God found in the Holy Bible. During this debate, Dr Login, a devout Christian, had intervened and said: 'On my part, I am subtly introducing the truth of the gospel to the boy, and am sure I will succeed. He is very keen on visiting England, and I am going to use that as bait for him to accept the Christian faith.' Both Sir Henry Lawrence and his brother John Lawrence expressed their opinion that it would be best to send the young maharaja away to England as soon as possible so that there could be no chance of rebellion by his mother Maharani Jindan Kaur and the loyal Sikhs. Dalhousie, however, made it clear that he did not want the statute against evangelisation violated in any way. The Court of Director of the Company had issued strict orders that religious neutrality should be maintained in India, and only voluntary conversions were to be permitted.

Consequently, Dr Jeaffreson was pleased with the steps he had already taken to facilitate permission for Veerarajendra to visit London. A week before Christmas that year, Dr Jeaffreson was back in Benares while on his way to Calcutta.

He made a quick detour to Coorg Nest and gave a detailed report to Veerarajendra about his visit to Lahore and the discussions he had with Dr John Login. He said to the raja, 'You need to make an announcement that your daughter Princess Gowramma will embrace Christianity. We will have to take steps to ensure this news reaches as many high-ranking British officers as possible. It will be welcomed, and they will all support your proposal, already with the governor-general, to grant you permission to accompany the child to England. You will indeed be the first royalty in India to take this bold step.' He explained to Veerarajendra about Maharaja Duleep Singh, and the plans Dr Login had in mind for the young deposed ruler.

With only a moment's contemplation, Veerarajendra said: 'Umm, Jeaffresonji, I endorse my decision that my dear daughter Gowramma become a Christian, given an education in English and raised in the manner of the children of the British aristocrats. As a Christian convert, this child of mine will be eligible to marry an English nobleman.'

Dr Jeaffreson's reply was spontaneous: 'May be we could work out an alliance between your little princess and the young maharaja from Punjab who is being indoctrinated to embrace Christianity.' Veerarajendra beamed with delight at the suggestion.

Inwardly though, the raja was troubled as he recalled his hatred for the British whom he had vociferously accused of spreading their faith in India. It seemed ironic that he was now proposing his favourite daughter follow the very religion he had lambasted. However, he comforted himself with his departed wife Devammaji's words, 'Mahaswami, it is better to join your enemy if you cannot vanquish him.' He wondered if Devammaji would have approved of his plans for Gowramma.

By then, Lt Col Carpenter had been replaced by Captain G.H. Macgregor as the supervisor of Veerarajendra and his family. Captain Macgregor was also in charge of Maharani Jindan Kaur who was under detention in Benares at the time. Dr Jeaffreson broached the subject of the Coorg princess with Captain Macgregor. As anticipated, Captain Macgregor and his staff welcomed the prospect of a member of the Indian royalty voluntarily embracing Christianity. He readily came forward to assist in educating the young Princess in the English language and groom her in Western culture and etiquettes. Captain Macgregor's wife agreed to be the governess.

Thus, Gowramma began her education; she would walk over next door to the home of the Macgregors' where Mrs Macgregor continued the tutoring in English started by Mrs Carpenter. A more thorough instruction in the scriptures also formed an integral part of the education. Gowramma took to her lessons in all earnestness and proved to be an enthusiastic learner. She was the only daughter of the raja to be dressed in frocks and skirts provided by her British tutors and soon became the envy of all her half-brothers and sisters.

During the last week of December 1849, Lord Dalhousie made a brief halt at Benares on his way back to Calcutta from his visit to Sindh and Punjab in the Northwest. The governor-general was pleased at the news that Veerarajendra, on his own volition, had confirmed that his daughter would embrace the Christian faith. On Captain Macgregor's suggestion, Lord Dalhousie agreed to meet Veerarajendra and Princess Gowramma for dinner. The governor-general was impressed at the progress made by the little princess since their last meeting. She spoke much better English, and with more confidence. Dalhousie assured the raja that he would pursue his request for permission to visit England. However, Dalhousie did not quite relish the idea of the raja travelling to England.

By March next year, eight-year-old Gowramma or Gowru, as she was fondly known, could read and write simple words in English. Mrs Macgregor encouraged Gowru to socialise with her children, and those of other British officers in Benares. Gowru was invited frequently to the homes of the British families in and around Benares, and soon took a liking to European food. However, in accordance with her father's instructions she refused to touch beef. Her favourite was plum cake and homemade biscuits. She conducted herself like a proper young English lass while having tea and cake with her British friends. With Mrs Macgregor's assistance, Gowramma also learnt to deftly use cutlery like the spoon, fork and knife.

The orthodox Hindus in Benares resented Veerarajendra's high-handedness in allowing his young daughter to behave like the feringhees. They made it known that the princess had broken her caste by drinking tea and eating cake with the white memsahibs. But what appalled them was the blasphemous proclamation by Veerarajendra that his daughter would soon embrace Christianity! Some of the priests threatened to ex-communicate the raja.

Much to the chagrin of Captain Stewart and other British officers, the determined mother of Duleep Singh, Jindan Kaur, who had been shifted from Benares to Chunar, had escaped from her detention on 18 April 1849 disguised as a *fakirnee*, a female mendicant, and fled to Nepal. The prime minister of Nepal, Jung Bahadur Rana, gave her asylum and provided her accommodation at

Kathmandu, though she had to pay for all comforts. However, after pressure from the East India Company, she was kept under house arrest in a haveli close to Jung Bahadur's palace. Dr Jeaffreson and Veerarajendra followed these developments with great interest.

In the meantime, the British intercepted the details of a plot hatched by Jindan Kaur and her loyal Khalsa supporters to rescue their young king by kidnapping him. The governor-general and the Resident at Punjab decided to move Duleep Singh away from Lahore. Sir Henry Lawrence, his brother John Lawrence and Dr Login had lengthy discussions to locate a secure place for the deposed Maharaja and some of his close family members.

Sir Henry Lawrence was the first to suggest Fatehgarh, a small settlement on the banks of the Ganges, about 100 miles from both Lucknow and Kanpur. Dr Login readily supported the idea as he was familiar with Fatehgarh where there was an American-Presbyterian Christian missionary named 'Fatehgarh Mission.' The mission, established in 1837, had a separate village of Indian-Christian converts. Most of the converted Indians were orphans who had been rescued during the famine of 1837. The missionaries were successfully running schools in the vernacular as well as English medium in the campus. A Presbyterian church was established in Fatehgarh, from where evangelic activities were effectively carried out. Several trades were taught to the residents in the village. Carpet-making was one of the main activities. They all concurred that the atmosphere in Fatehgarh would be highly conducive for its Christian influence on the impressionable Duleep Singh.

The journey from Lahore to Fatehgarh of the young maharaja of Punjab and his followers was a major military manoeuvre. Dr John Login was in charge of the entire operation. Governor-General Dalhousie provided adequate security to thwart any attempts of 'kidnap' by Rani Jindan Kaur and her Khalsa supporters. The camping sites en route were selected after careful consideration of strategic location and security. The camps were a display of colourful royal red and white marquees with the famed silver poles originally used by Ranjit Singh supporting the tents. On 19 February 1850, the entourage reached their destination after spending a little more than a month on the road.

Veerarajendra was excited when Jeaffreson brought the news of Maharaja Duleep Singh's arrival at Fatehgarh. He hoped he would be able to obtain permission from Captain Macgregor to visit Fatehgarh, situated about 300 miles away, to meet the young prince of Punjab.

It also dawned on Veerarajendra that by relocating the young sovereign, the wily British had completed the process of annexation of the Punjab. They had successfully followed their time-tested strategy of removing the deposed rulers away from their kingdom. Veerarajendra saw the similarity in his and the young maharaja's predicament, though he was aware of the vast difference between the size and wealth of their respective kingdoms.

An old manor located in a large estate in Fatehgarh on the elevated banks of the Ganges was selected as the residence of the twelve-year-old Maharaja Duleep Singh. His stepbrother's widow Rani Duknu and her six-year-old son Shahzadah Sahdev Singh had accompanied him. Dr John Login arranged a teenage English boy named Tommy Scott, son of a Company officer, to be a companion for the young maharaja. Robbie Carshore, the son of the Parish priest in Fatehgarh, was one more playmate of Duleep Singh. Dr Login named the establishment 'Fatehgarh Park'.

The building, earlier used by a British officer, had been lying vacant for many years and needed a great deal of renovation to make it fit for the son of the 'Lion of Punjab'. Comparing this residence to the citadel at Lahore was like comparing a goat to an elephant. Dr Login had the manor refurbished in record time for the maharaja to move in. Several other buildings in the sprawling compound were renovated to accommodate the large entourage of the deposed maharaja of Punjab. Rani Duknu and her son Sahdev Singh occupied a nearby mansion. The stunningly beautiful Rani Duknu, a Rajput by birth, was accompanied by her brother and an uncle. The young Maharaja Duleep Singh was pleased with the place since it was ideal for training his falcons.

In a letter to Sir Henry Lawrence, written on 16 July 1850, Dr Login detailed the progress his ward Maharaja Duleep Singh was making since their arrival at Fatehgarh. Knowing that by the age of six, Indian royalties were often married, the doctor had started scouting for a suitable bride for Duleep Singh. Lord Dalhousie had already made it clear that the bride should not be a Sikh. Dr Login wrote:

...I have been making enquires about a wife for my little boy. He says I am his 'Ma-Bap,' and he trusts me to do what may be necessary for his happiness. He will have nothing to do, he says, with Shere Singh's sister (daughter of Raja Chutter Singh), to whom he was betrothed, so I am quite at liberty to choose for him. I have heard of a little daughter of the Rajah of Coorg at Benares. She is being educated like an English child, and her father has asked and obtained permission to take her to England to have her education completed. She is only eight year of age, described as fair and good-looking and also intelligent with decided marks of good lineage about her. The father is not aware of my enquires. My informant is Major Stewart, the Governor-General's Agent at Benares who says that altogether he does not think my young protégé could anywhere get a more suitable wife! When I have heard from Macgregor and others who know her, I shall send my information to Lord Dalhousie privately. Possibly the matter may be so far arranged by the time you come out, that you may see her as the Maharajah's fiancée as you pass through Benares. There will be four years between their ages nearly. I have an idea, however, that young Duleep would prefer someone nearer his own age, and I may have some difficulty in the matter...

Dr John Login left Fatehgarh for Calcutta in November on a month's leave to meet his wife Lena, who was returning to India after almost two years. In his absence, Captain J. Campbell was appointed the acting 'Governor' of the maharaja. It was during this period that the young Duleep Singh took a radical decision which was to have a profound effect on his future.

A few months after their arrival at Fatehgarh, Duleep Singh had requested Dr Login for an Indian educated in English, as one of his companions. He wanted to interact with a native who was familiar with Western education. Duleep Singh was also keen on exchanging ideas about religions in India and comparing them with what he had learnt about Christianity. Dr Login found an ideal candidate from the Fatehgarh Mission—a young Brahmin named Bhajan Lal, one of the first Indians to be educated in the school run by the American Presbyterian Mission. He was intelligent, well-read, and a firm believer in Hinduism. However, having read the Bible, he also appreciated many aspects of Christianity. Bhajan Lal was happy to be in the company of the young maharaja who bombarded him with questions about Hinduism, Sikhism and Christianity.

Though Bhajan Lal had a reasonably good understanding of the Bible, he needed to refresh his knowledge, which he did by reading a copy of the Holy Book that had been gifted to Duleep Singh by Dr Login. While Dr Login was away in Calcutta, the young maharaja asked Bhajan Lal to explain to him about Christianity and some of the practices of Hinduism and Sikhism. He would often hurl questions at Bhajan Lal, seeking to understand the true essence of the two religions. Some of his queries would be like: 'Tell me Bhajan Lalji, will one wash away the sins committed by bathing in the Ganges? Will one go to heaven after a dip in the holy river?'

Bhajan Lal's replies were unfortunately not too convincing. He would reply thus: 'Yes maharaja, it is written as such in our ancient *Shastras*. But it all depends on the good we do during our lifetime. We believe in multiple gods, while the Bible says that there is only one Supreme Being. We worship idols, but Christianity is against the practice. Hindus believe in rebirth, whereas the Bible says one goes to heaven or hell depending on the verdict on judgment day.'

One of the teachings of the Bible, which impressed Duleep Singh, was that all human beings are born equal and that there are no superior or inferior castes. Duleep Singh kept repeating, 'We are all children of God. Jesus Christ is our saviour. The Holy Father has made us in his image.' The maharaja turned deeply reflective of God, religion and the life hereafter. One of the stories from the scriptures that moved Duleep Singh was the one where St Stephen was stoned to death. The young maharaja wept as Bhajan Lal read the story to him. He said: 'I am convinced this religion is true. Jesus Christ is our redeemer.'

Dr Login was still to return from Calcutta. One day Duleep Singh summoned Bhajan Lal and announced, 'I have decided to renounce the Sikh religion and embrace Christianity.' Bhajan Lal advised Duleep Singh not to take any hasty actions, especially since his guardian Dr Login was out of station. Disregarding Bhajan Lal's advice, Duleep Singh went on to inform Captain J. Campbell his intentions. The startling news was immediately communicated to Dr Login in Calcutta, who, in turn conveyed the details of the developments to Lord Dalhousie. The governor-general directed the doctor to hasten to Fatehgarh along with his wife Lena who had arrived a few days earlier. Dalhousie wanted a thorough investigation and a report to confirm that no pressure had been applied on the young maharaja in his decision to change religion. Furthermore, Dalhousie gave strict instructions to Dr Login not to make any public announcements until he had an opportunity to inform the Court of Directors at London and obtained their opinion.

With the retainer that Dr Jeaffreson received from Veerarajendra, he was able to take long furlough from his duties as a doctor in Bombay. His determination to help the raja of Coorg increased the more he saw the brazen exploitation of the locals by the British East India Company. During a short stay in Bombay, Dr Jeaffreson met a young official of the Company, Major Evans Bell, who was an assistant commissioner at Nagpur. Major Bell held even stronger views than Dr Jeaffreson regarding the high-handedness of the British in treating the rulers of the land and the general population. Major Bell was highly critical of the handling of the infant Maharaja Duleep Singh and wrote several articles which were published in leading newspapers in London. He openly expressed his opinion about the Indian Civil Service being full of supercilious young men from England. Major Bell was warned by the Company and when despite the admonishments he did not relent, he was charged with insubordination and dismissed from his assignment.

Major Evans Bell returned to England, but kept in touch with Dr Jeaffreson. He continued to write about British rule in India, and his views had significant effect on the liberal intellectuals of England. The impeachment and 'honourable' exoneration of the some of the questionable dealing of governor-general Warrer Hastings was still fresh in the minds of the people. Hastings was accused of having acquired finances in excess of his allowances. His devious methods in dealing with the raja of Benares, the begums of Oudh, and judicial murders of Indian notables had come under probe. There was growing outrage against the government for allowing such blatant injustice to continue unchecked in a colony. These activities were against the lofty ideals of the British, who took pride in calling themselves the most civilised and enlightened in the world.

Another Englishman, F.J. Shore, son of Sir John Shore, the governor-general during the last decade of the eighteenth century, had also written a highly critical analysis of the British administration, and in his book published in 1837 made the following observation:

> The halcyon days of India are over; she has been drained of a large proportion of the wealth she once possessed; and her energies have been cramped by a sordid system of misrule to which the interests of millions have been sacrificed for the benefit of the few.

He lamented about the behaviour of British soldiers, administrators and traders who predominantly came from the middle-class society in England. As the power of the East India Company grew, especially after the annexation of Punjab, these relatively unqualified British exhibited racist and prejudiced attitude towards the Indians.

Dr Jeaffreson lost no time in visiting Dr John Login at Fatehgarh. By then Lena Login had joined her husband. The young maharaja seemed happy in his new environment and was busy training his falcons when Dr Jeaffreson met him. The countryside was ideal for Duleep Singh to indulge in horseriding and his favourite passion of hunting birds with his trained falcons.

Dr Login and Lena Login were fascinated to hear from Dr Jeaffreson about the tiny kingdom of Coorg which had been annexed by the Company more than a decade earlier. The story of the exiled raja and his zeal to obtain a European education for his young daughter interested them immensely. Dr Jeaffreson told the Logins about the similarity between Scotland and the tiny province of Coorg, as well as his observation that the locals had many aspects in common with the highlanders. The Logins wanted to know more, and their interest was further aroused on hearing the raja's plans for his favourite daughter to embrace Christianity. Dr Jeaffreson, however, kept the issue of Veerarajendra's intentions of filing a suit against the East India Company to himself.

'John, I am lending a helping hand to Veerarajendra in his quest for permission to take his young daughter to England so that she can be baptized there and raised as a Christian with proper British education.' Dr Jeaffreson added, 'No other Indian royalty has taken this bold step until now. I want you to put in a word to Lord Dalhousie.'

Dr Login was pleased at the turn of events. The Coorg princess had already crossed his mind in his scheme for the maharaja's future. During their conversation, Dr Jeaffreson also said to Dr Login, 'Veerarajendra is keen on meeting Maharaja Duleep Singh and is interested in proposing an alliance with the young maharaja for his daughter Gowramma since both have similar background.'

Lena Login spontaneously exclaimed, 'What a splendid proposal! It will be a perfect marriage and a wonderful boost for Christianity in India.'

The Logins attributed these developments, which meshed perfectly with their own plans, to divine providence. They firmly believed that the British were ordained to spread the word of the Bible amongst the pagan worshippers of India. They now had strong reasons to facilitate the visit of Veerarajendra and his daughter to England. Maharaja Duleep Singh was already being groomed to live in England as a nobleman, and if the proposed alliance with the Coorg princess was successful, then the entire exercise would serve as a catalyst in promoting Christianity in India.

4

JOURNEY TO ENGLAND

Veerarajendra's request for permission to visit England received a substantial boost with the Logins strongly recommending the case to Lord Dalhousie. The Resident at Lucknow, Colonel William Sleeman, too gave his assurance to the Logins to help their cause by taking up the matter with influential officers in the India Office.

During Lord William Bentinck's regime, Colonel Sleeman had become famous for successfully taming the notorious thugs who stalked the pilgrims mainly in central and eastern parts of India. He also took an active part in Lord Bentinck's crusade against sati, an endeavour in which he was ably supported by reformer Raja Ram Mohan Roy. Colonel Sleeman shared the Logins' belief that nothing but the teaching of the Gospel could dispel the ignorance and primitive beliefs prevalent in India.

Sleeman too was of the view that both Maharaja Duleep Singh's and the Coorg princess' decision to embrace Christianity was a positive step and augured well for India. The Logins were happy to hear Sleeman say, 'We need to support this cathartic change, and help in the union of these two members of the native royalty. Their being educated in England will expose them to the civilised society of the West. On their return, they will be in a better position to appreciate and popularise Western culture and technological progress in India. In the long term, this is the best strategy to dispel some of the horrendous superstitions rampant in this vast country.'

Around this time, in neighbouring Nepal, the thirty-four-year-old Jung Bahadur had taken absolute control of his country as the prime minister. He had offered Maharaja Duleep Singh's mother Jindan Kaur an asylum, but restricted her movements on instructions from the British. Four years earlier, he had deposed King Rajendra Bikram Shah of Nepal and had elevated the king's young and pliable son Surendra Bikram Shah to the throne. The deposed king and his family were exiled to Benares. However, when Jung Bahadur found the king plotting against him, he took him back to Nepal where he was imprisoned with no access to the outside world.

Jung Bahadur visited Calcutta and Benares frequently, and had befriended many influential British officers. Sir Henry Lawrence was the Resident in the Court of Nepal during the turmoil and knew Jung Bahadur well. The Nepalese prime minister had formalised a strategic alliance with the East India Company who used him as a bulwark against the Chinese. Yet, one person strongly averse to Jung Bahadur's rising power was Lord Dalhousie, who branded him a usurper and an untrustworthy ally.

Jung Bahadur had forged several matrimonial alliances between his children and the royal family of Nepal. He entertained the possibility of marriage of one of his daughters with Maharaja Duleep Singh. Though not very enthusiastic initially, Rani Jindan Kaur too felt it may be a good alliance. 'Bahadurji, I am worried for my son who is already twelve years old and still unmarried. The British have kidnapped him and are forcing him to embrace their religion and marry a white girl,' she agonised to Jung Bahadur. 'My son was engaged to the daughter of Raja Chutter Singh, but the feringhees did not allow the marriage to take place.' Jung Bahadur had also heard the rumours that the British were planning to shift Duleep Singh to England.

Jung Bahadur soon learnt from his spies in Benares that the British were scheming to bring about an alliance between Duleep Singh and the daughter of the exiled raja of Coorg. He also received reports of the young Princess Gowramma being trained to be baptised as a Christian.

During one of his frequent visits to Calcutta, Lucknow and Benares, Jung Bahadur made a brief detour to Fatehgarh to meet Duleep Singh and Dr John Login. Maharani Jindan Kaur had pleaded with him to get news about her son. He also wanted to meet the influential Dr John Login whose brother Dr James Dryburgh Login was the Assistant Resident in Kathmandu. By then, the young maharaja had taken the decision to embrace Christianity. Jung Bahadur was shocked when he heard this from Duleep Singh himself. He tried to advise the boy: 'You are the son of the great Maharaja Ranjit Singh whose valour is known to the entire world. You should not break caste and defile your brave father's name. Your mother is worried. This news will surely break her heart. Maharaja, I offer my daughter to you in marriage, but if you change your religion it will not be possible.'

Duleep Singh was indifferent and said: 'I do not wish to continue to follow Indian religions which are full of superstitions and illogical practices.' The Logins, on the other hand, were elated at the young maharaja's resolve.

By now, Jung Bahadur was curious to make the acquaintance of the raja of Coorg, and he requested an interview with Veerarajendra. Veerarajendra was elated at the unexpected visit of the powerful prime minister of Nepal to his humble abode. He greeted Jung Bahadur warmly, and they exchanged pleasantries and spoke at length about hunting—a sport both enjoyed. They also found commonality in the fact that Veerarajendra, belonging to the Lingayat sect and Jung Bahadur as worshipper of Pashupathinath, were both devotees of Lord Siva.

Jung Bahadur recounted to the raja his visit to Fatehgarh and his subsequent meeting with Duleep Singh. He caught Veerarajendra's interest by hinting at the rumour of a likely alliance between the Maharaja Duleep Singh and the Coorg princess. When Jung Bahadur expressed his desire to meet Princess Gowramma, his request was readily granted. Gowramma's half-sister Gangamma too came along to meet their important visitor. The two nine-year-old princesses were a study in contrasts—Princess Gowramma had donned her usual European attire while Princess Gangamma was dressed in traditional *lehenga* and blouse.

The ruler of Nepal complimented Veerarajendra, 'Your daughters are very beautiful, I beseech you not to allow them to abandon our Hindu *dharma* in favour of Christianity.' Veerarajendra shook his head vehemently. 'It's only Princess

Gowramma who will be converting. All my other children will remain Hindus.'

The strongman of Nepal was instantly smitten by the striking good looks of Princess Gangamma, whom Lord Dalhousie too had found extraordinarily beautiful. The vast differences in their ages was hardly an impediment to Jung Bahadur, for it was considered normal for girls to be married by age ten, and powerful men had no upper age-limit.

The meetings with Maharaja Duleep Singh and the raja of Coorg prompted an idea in the mind of the prime minister of Nepal. He too wished to visit England, meet Queen Victoria, and study the progress in the Western world. Above all, he wanted to consolidate his country's cordial relationships with the British government.

When Lord Dalhousie heard of Jung Bahadur's plans to visit London, he was livid and commented: 'I don't want that grandee visiting England to make a fool of himself and the Company.' But Jung Bahadur's British friends including Sir Henry Lawrence supported the visit, and felt that it would be good publicity for the image of the Company, which was being tarnished by some of the liberals at home. When this proposal reached the Court of Directors in London, a majority of the members favoured the visit of Jung Bahadur to Britain. Lord Dalhousie's opposition was overruled. Dr John Login's brother, Dr James Dryburgh Login, who was well acquainted with Jung Bahadur, was selected by the government of India to accompany the prime minister during the expedition from Calcutta to London and back. Unfortunately, even before the news could reach Dr James Login, he contracted cholera while away on duty at Dinapore, and succumbed to the disease within a day.

Permission for Prime Minister Jung Bahadur to sail to London came earlier than expected. Nepal, being an ally of the British, helped, and the prime minister was all set to visit England even before Veerarajendra's impending journey. In April 1850, he boarded the ship at Calcutta. Nepal had a strategic partnership with the British, despite not being a part of the Company's territory. The officials of the East India Company received Jung Bahadur and two of his brothers who were part of the delegation, with all the cordiality due to visiting dignitaries. The East India Company threw a grand banquet in his honour on 15 June 1850. On 20 June, Jung Bahadur was overjoyed when the queen granted him an audience, where he presented a symbolic letter from the King of Nepal to Her Majesty, the queen. The queen invited the Nepali strongman to a State Ball at Buckingham Palace, where nearly 2,000 guests were present.

Jung Bahadur was highly impressed by the spectacular progress in Europe. The British government arranged for him to visit factories, railway networks, telegraph systems, mines and other modern undertakings. After inspecting these massive projects, his resolve to have close ties with the British was further reinforced. He was determined to continue as a strategic ally of the British, and sought their assistance to improve economic conditions in Nepal. This alliance proved crucial for the British during their hour of need a few years later in 1857, in spite of the ambivalent attitude of Lord Dalhousie towards Jung Bahadur.

During his journey back, Jung Bahadur made a brief visit to Paris as well. On his return to Nepal in February the following year, he began to adopt the lifestyle of the Europeans, and tried to implement their progressive policies in his country. He practically abolished death penalty, except in very rare cases. He also made it his mission to eliminate the practice of sati.

Within a month of his return from England, he made a brief trip to Benares to meet the raja of Coorg for a specific purpose—to seek the hand of Princess Gangamma in marriage. During the previous year that he was away, his infatuation had grown manifold and he now wanted to wed her.

The prime minister bowed and paid respectful obeisance to Veerarajendra, who was quite taken aback by the show of such humility from the strongman of Nepal. Jung Bahadur narrated his experiences in Britain and waxed eloquently about the amazing progress there. He spoke at length about the great city of London where more than two million people lived. The congested streets were full of horse carriages; more and more villagers were flocking into London and other cities in search of jobs in the numerous factories. However, Londoners were recovering from a deadly epidemic of cholera. Jung Bahadur spoke at length about the industrial units, the railways, roads, tunnels and the telegraph system. He described the preparations afoot for the Great London Exhibition. 'I was told that the Maharaja Duleep Singh's Koh-i-noor diamond would be on display at the exhibition,' he added.

After speaking in glowing terms about the British, Jung Bahadur said rather apologetically, 'Maharaja, I have bathed in the holy Ganges to purify myself for having crossed the seas and having dined with the feringhees.'

He then suddenly stood up and said with folded hands, 'Your Highness, maharaja of Coorg, I seek your consent to take your daughter, Rajkumari Gangamma, as my wife. I promise to take good care of her.' Veerarajendra was speechless. He quickly recovered and raised Jung Bahadur who knelt in front of him

Jung Bahadur's power and influence in Nepal was well known. Veerarajendra could hardly conceal his excitement; the alliance would be a great boost to his image.

'I will be happy to give my dear daughter Gangamma to you in marriage.' After a moment's contemplation he added, 'I would like the wedding celebrations to happen before I undertake my voyage to London with my daughter Gowramma.'

Jung Bahadur touched Veerarajendra's feet and promised to return to Benares in a few months to formalise the marriage alliance. 'As soon as I reach Kathmandu, I will consult my astrologers to fix an auspicious day for the betrothal.' For Jung Bahadur it was a routine affair; he was accustomed to taking a new wife almost once in every six months.

Subadhramma and her daughter, the young Princess Gangamma, were summoned to meet the ruler of Nepal. Subadhramma was elated at the proposal and was overawed when Jung Bahadur stooped and touched her feet. Princess Gangamma, barely ten years old, was bewildered by these unexpected developments. Just then, Princess Gowramma walked into the room to see all the attention being showered on her sister; it was a rare occasion indeed when Gowramma found herself overshadowed by Gangamma. Jung Bahadur had brought presents from London for Veerarajendra, Subadhramma and his young bride-to-be, Gangamma. For the raja, he presented a woollen overcoat and said, 'Maharaja, you will need this to keep you warm and dry during your visit to London.' He gifted a strand of pearls to Subadhramma. He had brought jewellery, sweaters and dolls for Gangamma. He also had gifts for all the wives and the remaining children of the raja. There was great rejoicing in Coorg Nest that day.

For Veerarajendra, it was a long-awaited moment of sheer happiness since his exile from Kodagu seventeen years ago. He now felt confident that his mission to London would yield the desired result.

Ever since his announcement that his chosen daughter Princess Gowramma was to embrace Christianity, British families in and around Benares vied with one another to be friends of Veerarajendra. Many came visiting Coorg Nest along with their children. They were interested in meeting the ten-year-old princess. Most of the visitors were ardent followers of the Church of England. Veerarajendra and Gowramma received invitations from British families to visit their homes to break bread with them.

During this time, Governor-General Lord Dalhousie was monitoring Princess Gowramma's progress and preparation for her baptism. He was also keeping a close watch on Maharaja Duleep Singh whose preparation for initiation into the Christian faith was progressing satisfactorily in Fatehgarh under the tutelage of Dr John and Lena Login.

However, Lord Dalhousie reacted angrily on reading widely publicised reports of the visit of Jung Bahadur to England. He disapproved of the undue importance given to the prime minister of Nepal. Dalhousie was not in favour of Indian nobles visiting England. He firmly believed that the Eastern behaviour would clash with the Western way of life and culture. Just as he had opposed Jung Bahadur's voyage to England, he expressed his strong resentments at Veerarajendra's proposed visit. He did not mind Princess Gowramma visiting London. However, since Princess Gowramma was a minor, she had to be accompanied by her father. With recommendations coming from various quarters

Lord Dalhousie reluctantly gave his consent for Veerarajendra and Princess Gowramma to visit England.

Queen Victoria had been briefed about the Indian princess from Coorg, and her eagerly-awaited conversion to Christianity on reaching English soil. Her Majesty and her consort, Prince Albert, were delighted at the prospect of a member of the Indian royalty voluntarily coming into the Christian fold. They also looked forward to the arrival of Maharaja Duleep Singh who had emphatically announced his desire to discard his religion and take the path shown by Jesus Christ.

Maharaja Duleep Singh's education in English made satisfactory progress under the guidance of the Login couple. He was being taught how to conduct himself like an English nobleman. As his knowledge of English grew, Duleep Singh read with great fascination the *Boys' Own Book*, presented to him by the Logins. Written by 'John Uncle', the book was a best seller in America and Britain. It described in detail various games popular with youngsters. The book also gave interesting information about birds and animals. The maharaja played several of the games mentioned in the book with his European friends Tommy Scott and Robbie Carshore, and his nephew Sahdev Singh.

The Logins enthusiastically encouraged the 'voluntary' proclamation of the young maharaja to follow the Gospel. Dalhousie was happy, but was rather apprehensive of any compulsions, which might have forced the young maharaja in taking his drastic decision. The Sikhs and Maharani Jindan Kaur would certainly make an outcry at this development and would blame the British for taking advantage of an immature prince. Maharaja Duleep Singh was considered the head of the Khalsa, the highest temporal authority of the Sikhs. But by then,

Duleep Singh openly expressed, 'I do not like my mother. She used to ill-treat me when I was young. I have no faith in my religion. I wholeheartedly renounce it.'

For the record, Dalhousie wanted concrete proof from the Logins to confirm that they had not directly influenced Duleep Singh's decision. Dr Login therefore asked Bhajan Lal to write down the events that had led to Duleep Singh's announcement about renouncing his religion and embracing Christianity. Bhajan Lal wrote a lengthy report of what happened in Fatehgarh Park when Dr Login was away in Calcutta to receive his wife Lena during November 1850. The report was then sent to the governor-general, who, after reading the narrative pronounced that he was 'entirely satisfied that no improper influence was used either directly or indirectly by any of the English staff in charge of the maharaja.'

In his report, Bhajan Lal had elaborated the events that occurred in Fatehgarh Park during Dr Login's absence. The young maharaja was firm in his decision to break away from the religion of his birth. To reinforce his resolve, he had invited his English friends Tommy Scott and Robbie Carshore to his mansion, where to his friends' astonishment, the maharaja boiled water and prepared tea for all of them. Bhajan Lal tried to persuade Duleep Singh not to take such an important decision when Dr Login was away. Duleep Singh was, however, determined, and with a flourish, offered tea to his English friends and joined them in drinking the beverage. The conservative Hindus and the Sikhs considered drinking tea with the white man blasphemous. The deed was synonymous with breaking one's caste.

Lord Dalhousie was quite pleased when he received the details of Duleep Singh's intentions and his drinking tea with Tommy

Scott. He, however, did not publicly express his delight. To his friend, Sir George Couper in England, he wrote:

> My little friend Duleep has taken us all aback lately by declaring his resolution to become a Christian. The pundits, he says, tell him humbug. He has had the Bible read to him, and he believes the Sahib's religion. The household, of course, are in a grand state. Politically we could desire nothing better, for it destroys his possible influence for ever. But I should have been glad if it had been deferred, since at present it may be represented to have been brought about by tampering with the mind of a child. This is not the case, it is his own free act, and apparently his firm resolution. He will be a Christian, he says; 'and he will take tea with Tommy Scott,' which his caste has hitherto prevented! This last cause is a comical point in his profession of faith! I have thought it right to report the thing to the Court of Directors for their orders. But, as you may suppose, I have intimated that if the lapse of time shall show that this is not a fantasy of the boy, that he knows the effects of what he is doing and still persists in his desire to be instructed in Christian truths, I can be no party to discouraging, still less to opposing it. He is a remarkable boy in many ways.

As expected, when the news of Duleep Singh's imminent conversion and his voyage to England reached his mother Jindan Kaur, she flew into a rage. Jung Bahadur, who gave her the details, had to face the fury of the maharani. The strongman of Nepal and the mercurial wife of Ranjit Singh had frequent and noisy fights. Jindan Kaur was barely in her twenties when she had married the 'Lion of Punjab'. Though a commoner, she was known for her beauty, wit and intelligence. She was said to possess the most captivating pair of eyes. Jindan Kaur was accustomed to having her way as the favourite wife of the powerful Ranjit Singh, and later she played a significant role in ruling Punjab for nearly four years as Regent to her minor son. In order to curtail her influence on the Sikhs, the British spread gossip to denigrate her character. The British, and Dalhousie in particular, gave publicity to salacious rumours of Jindal Kaur's promiscuity. They slyly gave credence to the hearsay that Ranjit Singh was not the real father of Duleep Singh. Subtle hints of these scandalous rumours were fed to Duleep Singh. The impressionable Maharaja started to dislike his own mother. On one occasion, he said to Dr John Login, 'I wish I could put her to death for discrediting my father. That is the just punishment for crimes of this nature.' Dr Login, a devout Christian, however failed to instil in the impressionable Maharaja one of the defining teachings of his religion—'Honour thy father and mother.'

During their raucous encounters, Jindan Kaur mocked Jung Bahadur as 'a lackey of the British.' Jung Bahadur made light of this accusation and said, 'Maybe, but I stand to gain immensely from this alliance with the white man. I have seen their land, their progress, and the power they wield. It is unwise to fight them. Instead, I want to get the best from them for the benefit of my country and people.'

Jindan Kaur jeered at him, 'Mark my words, they will betray you just as they have done to my innocent son, and to so many of the kingdoms in Hindustan.'

Lambasting Dalhousie's infamous Doctrine of Lapse, maharani Jindan Kaur said to Jung Bahadur, 'He is a treacherous man who has repeatedly gone back on treaties and annexed vast territories. See, he has just swallowed the kingdom of Oudh.'

But Jung Bahadur tried to justify the British actions. 'Dalhousie is introducing the railways, the telegraph system, postal services and building good roads all over Hindustan. He has also opened universities and the common man is living in relative peace,' he argued.

Jung Bahadur tried in vain to console the tearful maharani. She wanted to know why Jung Bahadur was not offering one of his daughters in marriage to her son. She also demanded more funds from Jung Bahadur for her expenses. Soon after annexation of the Punjab, the British had accused Jindan Kaur of plotting to assassinate the Resident of Punjab, Sir Henry Lawrence and his officers. Using this as a pretext the British had confiscated all her jewels and wealth. They also reduced her pension. She complained to the prime minister, 'The 20,000 rupees you give me annually on behalf of the British, is less than the *baksheesh* I paid my servants in a year in Punjab.'

Not wanting to prolong the diatribe, Jung Bahadur assured Jindan Kaur, 'I will be going to Benares soon and will take up the issue of your allowance with the British.' Maharani Jindan Kaur then ridiculed Jung Bahadur when he mentioned his forthcoming marriage to a daughter of the raja of Coorg.

When the news of the strongman of Nepal marrying Princess Gangamma reached Dalhousie, the latter was derisive. Dalhousie wished the angelic Gangamma too had followed Gowramma in receiving Western education and had been saved from joining the crowded harem of the rakish Jung Bahadur.

During mid-1851, Jung Bahadur finally came to Benares for his betrothal to Princess Gangamma. Veerarajendra could not afford a lavish ceremony in his modest haveli. The prime minister of Nepal had the nuptial rites performed by priests from the Siva temple in Benares. He would have an elaborate marriage ceremony in Kathmandu after his young bride came of age. He presented a gold-plated model of the famous Pashupatinath temple in Nepal to Veerarajendra, and said: 'Maharaja of Coorg, you have given me a most precious gift, the hand of your beautiful daughter. May Lord Pashupatinath bless us all.'

Veerarajendra was not one to show his emotions, but at that moment, he had tears in his eyes. He replied, 'I don't know when I will see my little Ganga again.'

Jung Bahadur promised to bring the princess to Benares whenever he travelled to the holy city. Gangamma bade a tearful farewell to her family as she got into Jung Bahadur's grand horse carriage for the long journey to her new home in Nepal. Jung Bahadur assured Veerarajendra and Subadhramma that Gangamma would be educated in the palace, and taught all that a wife of a ruler ought to know.

After the ceremonies, Veerarajendra sat on his rosewood chair, and took a deep breath. It was after a long time that he felt like a raja. His spirits were up. His daughter Gangamma would have a good life as the wife of Jung Bahadur Rana. Princess Gowramma could be a maharani if Maharaja Duleep Singh took her as his wife. If the alliance with Duleep Singh did not come about, he wanted his daughter to marry a European nobleman. That would ensure better relationship with the British authorities. He was excited about visiting England, and hoped to have an audience with the queen. Having heard so much from Jung Bahadur and his British friends about the sea voyage and the magnificent city of London, he was now looking forward to his journey. Judging by the chain of events in the recent past, the portents were good. He was sure that Laxmi, the goddess of wealth, would soon smile on him, and he would succeed in securing the investments worth more than twelve lakhs of rupees from the East India Company.

Back in the summer of 1849, Veerarajendra had another visitor from his erstwhile kingdom—Pirojirao, the son of Veerarajendra's court painter, Gangojirao. Pirojirao had journeyed to Benares after hearing stories from Alamanda Somayya. He wanted to meet the raja and his family, and visit all the holy places. Pirojirao himself was an accomplished painter. Veerarajendra asked him to stay on in Benares to paint portraits of himself and his family. By then there were two more additions to his family. He was now the father of seven sons and four daughters. The task of completing the family portraits took more than a year.

When Pirojirao was ready to get back to Coorg, Veerarajendra nostalgically told him, 'Pirojirao, before I leave on this voyage across the seas, I am yearning to hear our melodious *volaga*. When you reach Kodagu, please tell your father to arrange for my palace band to come here so that I could listen to them play for my family and me. None of my children have heard our volaga from Kodagu.'

Veerarajendra requested Captain Macgregor to write to the superintendent in Coorg at the time, Captain H.F. Gustard, to help the troupe to travel from his former kingdom to Benares. Captain Macgregor reasoned: 'Since you will be leaving for England soon, this request of yours could be taken up after your return a year later.'

A disappointed Veerarajendra replied, 'I am crossing the seas, and what if I do not return? I hear the voyage is fraught with danger.'

It was towards the end of 1851 that Dr William Jeaffreson next visited Benares to brief Veerarajendra about the voyage to

England. The next suitable ship to London was available only in February the following year. Dr Jeaffreson had secretly arranged in London for legal experts to take up the case of the raja against the East India Company. He advised the raja to limit the size of his entourage. The British appointed Major Drummond of the Third Bengal Cavalry and his wife to escort the raja during the long voyage from Calcutta to London.

The Drummonds were earlier posted in Benares, and had befriended Veerarajendra prior to the assignment. They were set to return to England on long furlough, and this assignment came at just the right time. The government of India insisted that Veerarajendra pay for the voyage and all the other travel expenses of the Drummonds. When Veerarajendra protested, Major W.M. Stewart threatened to withdraw permission for the trip; swallowing his pride, Veerarajendra had to accept.

Queen Victoria had informed Dalhousie about her desire to meet the princess from Coorg. Lord Dalhousie, therefore, instructed Mrs Drummond to begin tutoring Gowramma for her audience with Queen Victoria. Gowru was taught how to curtsy and to conduct herself in the presence of the royal family. Her knowledge of English had also improved vastly. Mrs Drummond began acquainting the young princess with English literature and history. Veerarajendra also had to learn some of the basic protocols of English society. He had to practise the proper use of cutlery since they would be attending state banquets. When the raja was told not to slurp and belch after a meal, he was a trifle puzzled and asked, 'How else do I show my appreciation of the food?'

Gowru, by now quite familiar with English etiquettes, told her father, 'Appa, it is considered highly impolite and primitive. Please do not embarrass me.'

'All right my pigeon, for your sake I will follow these silly customs of the white man,' Veerarajendra comforted his daughter.

Lord Dalhousie continued to express his unhappiness at 'the rascally raja of Coorg' visiting England. However, the Board of Directors of the East India Company were looking forward to the visit of the first royalty from India. The raja of Coorg's voluntary decision to encourage his favourite daughter to embrace Western ways and the Christian religion had excited British society. For the colonialists supported by the evangelists, the success of this visit would vastly influence the acceptance of Christianity and Western thoughts in India. Already, Jung Bahadur, the powerful ruler of Nepal, had returned to the Indian subcontinent, and was putting into practice some of the Western ideas. His decision to ban the practice of sati had received wide publicity in the British press. He had also virtually stopped capital punishment in his domain. He negotiated with the British for introduction of telegraph, railways and irrigation canals in his kingdom.

For the British, the imminent conversion and visit of the high profile maharaja of Punjab was another great event. Lord Dalhousie too wholeheartedly welcomed the idea of Maharaja Duleep Singh visiting England. He was eager to have the Sikh maharaja well away from India so that his followers, influenced by his dominant mother Jindan Kaur, did not regroup and pose a threat to the British. In the last three years since the annexation, there was normalcy in Punjab. The general populace was enjoying peace in their land after the two devastating wars with the British. Lord Dalhousie's vigorous efforts in introducing the railways, telegraph, better roads, irrigation canals and education had been well received by the progressive-minded Punjabis.

At Fatehgarh Park, the Logins had reasons to feel happy with Duleep Singh's progress. On instructions from Dalhousie, a tutor named Walter Guise was appointed to teach Duleep Singh. Initially Guise found it difficult to hold the young maharaja's attention and had to devise various means to interest Duleep Singh on diverse subjects commonly learnt by young European boys. His classes were interspersed with a liberal sprinkling of religious teachings and parables found in the Gospels. Duleep Singh's nephew Sahdev Singh too attended the classes given by Guise. However, Sahdev Singh's mother Rani Duknu was unhappy with Duleep Singh's preoccupation with the religion of the feringhees. Duleep Singh deliberately committed several deeds considered unholy by the Sikhs and the Hindus to show his resolve to make a clean break from his religion. Rani Duknu tried to keep her son away from the influence of the British and Duleep Singh. Nevertheless, she secretly rejoiced at the prospect of her son ultimately replacing Duleep Singh as successor to Ranjit Singh's legacy.

When the doctor's wife Lena Login joined them at Fatehgarh Park in December 1850, Duleep Singh took an instant liking to her. Lena had left her three young children back in England. She had come back to India to help her husband manage the affairs of the deposed maharaja. Both Dr Login and Lena Login found the young maharaja very endearing and affectionate. Their long stay in India had given them a good insight into the behaviour of the Indian royalty. The couple had established close friendship with the royal family of Oudh during their stay in Lucknow. They found the Indian rulers to be habitually indulgent and Duleep Singh was no exception.

Having sat on the throne of Punjab for three years as a young boy, Duleep Singh was accustomed to having his way all the time. It was the mission of the Login couple to bring about a change in the juvenile maharaja so that he would be more in tune with Western lifestyle. The Logins were quite familiar with the Indian languages as well, and Duleep Singh was comfortable under their care. Along with his tutor Walter Guise, the Logins began to groom Duleep Singh for a life enjoyed by the British nobility. Duleep Singh's interest was aroused when Dr Login assured him: 'If your grasp of the subjects being taught here improves, we can arrange for you to live in England for a few years to further your education.'

In keeping with Lord Dalhousie's philosophy, the Logins were engaged in the task of changing the mindset of the 'indolent Easterner rulers'. Duleep Singh's two English companions, Tommy Scott and Robbie Carshore, served the purpose of setting an example for the naïve maharaja to follow the British system of education. All these steps truly kindled Duleep Singh's interest in learning the subjects taught in British schools. He gradually started developing a liking for the English language, their literature, culture, and history. The *Boy's Own Book* by William Clarke had a profound impact on the young maharaja. When Duleep Singh's understanding of English improved, the Logins presented him another volume of the book, which detailed the scientific discoveries of the era. After reading these publications, Duleep Singh expressed his deep desire to visit England as soon as possible.

However, falconry remained his favourite sport and Duleep Singh spent a considerable amount of time training his birds of prey. During his outings, he was fond of carrying one of his trained falcons on his leather-gloved hand. Dr John and Lena Login found this preoccupation to be cruel, and tried to discourage

Duleep Singh from what they called 'blood sport'. They felt this activity developed a mean streak in the boy, which needed to be curbed.

Dr John Login was aware of the traumatic effect on Duleep Singh when as a six-years-old, the latter was witness to the brutal murder of his uncle, Jawahir Singh, the trusted brother of Maharani Jindan Kaur. Duleep Singh had vivid recollection of the fateful event in 1843 when he and his uncle, seated in the silver howdah atop the palace elephant, were suddenly attacked. Jawahir Singh was bludgeoned and shot to death and though Duleep Singh was unharmed, he was highly disturbed. The young maharaja had witnessed a great deal of violence during his formative years in Lahore. His half-brother and predecessor Maharaja Sher Singh was beheaded by rival Sikh chieftains. In Dr Login's opinion, these violent events contributed to the cruel streak in the youngster.

One of the daily rituals in the evenings at 'Fatehgarh Park' was a minor darbar in the young maharaja's drawing room. Few of the high-ranking officials from his court in Lahore, now living in Fatehgarh, would pay their obeisance to the deposed monarch who sat regally on a couch. After this formality, Duleep Singh indulged in games described in *Boy's Own Book*, such as hide-and-seek, blind man's bluff, the huntsman, puss in the corner, etc. It was also a daily routine for the young maharaja to go on an elephant ride, sitting in his silver howdah, accompanied by Sahdev Singh and his English friends, Robbie Carshore and Tommy Scott. His Sikh attendants, followed by the bodyguards provided by the governor-general, accompanied the cavalcade, dressed in their impressive uniform. Another favourite pastime was a ride in the magnificent four-horse carriage driven by his English coachman, Thornton. During these outings, he would have a hawk sitting on his outstretched gloved arm. An assistant was invariably kept nearby with pieces of meat for the bird. Bhajan Lal kept away from Duleep Singh whenever he indulged in this macabre sport.

With his determination to break his caste and embrace Christianity unshaken, Duleep Singh one day stunned Lena Login by cutting his long tresses. He then handed it to her saying, 'Lena, please accept my locks as my present to you and John.' Duleep Singh had earlier expressed his desire to look more like his English friends. All these defiant actions like drinking tea with the feringhees, shearing his hair, and above all the talk of embracing Christianity, had shocked the members of the Sikh Khalsa. They no longer considered Duleep Singh their sovereign. Rani Duknu saw this as an opportunity to project her young son Sahdev Singh, the nephew of Duleep Singh, as the next maharaja of Punjab and head of the Khalsa. When Dalhousie heard of this, he issued a severe warning to Rani Duknu not to entertain any such ambitions. He sent a stern message that any move to anoint a successor to Duleep Singh would be viewed as a crime against the British rule, and would result in severe repercussions.

After Lord Dalhousie was convinced by Dr John Login that Duleep Singh's decision to convert was voluntary, he asked Dr Login to step-up the teaching of the Bible so that the maharaja could be prepared for baptism. Dr Login found the right candidate to take up this task—Reverend Carshore.

In the meantime, Veerarajendra was ready for his long voyage beyond the seven seas along with his daughter Gowramma. Since he had to bear the travel cost of his escorts, the Drummonds, he had to limit the size of his entourage. After much debate in Coorg Nest, the raja selected one of his minor wives, the young Mudduveeramma, and an equally young concubine named Siddaveeramma to accompany him. The two women would also look after the household in London. His trusted assistant Munshi Shantamalla and cook Seetharamayya were also prepared for the trip along with two male servants. He had to set aside a part of his yearly pension of 60,000 rupees for maintaining his large family in Benares. He also had to meet the cost of living in London for a year, and the fees that he would have to pay his lawyers. He said to himself, 'If I succeed in getting the twelve lakh rupees, all my efforts would be worthwhile.'

His good friend Dr William Jeaffreson had assured the raja that legal experts whom he had already appointed in London would handle his case. He advised Veerarajendra, 'Don't be too hasty in taking up the legal issue on reaching London. Wait until Gowramma is well accepted by British society. A favourable public opinion is very important. I have received intelligence that the queen herself is eager to meet you and your daughter.'

Gowramma, now eleven-years-old, was quite conversant with Western etiquette and spoke English confidently. She had acquired poise and conducted herself admirably. Her British tutors were happy with the progress she had made, and were sure the young princess would make a noteworthy impact on English society on reaching London. Princess Gowramma was full of anticipation of her voyage and new life in British society. However, the prospect of Gowramma renouncing her religion to embrace Christianity affected Subadhramma deeply. She had heated arguments with Veerarajendra. She tried her best to prevent Gowru from crossing the forbidden seas.

'Gowru will lose her caste and no respectable family will want their sons to marry her,' bemoaned Subadhramma.

Veerarajendra tried to convince her by saying, 'Subadhra, I am doing this for the overall good of the family. I cannot give you all the details, but you will know when I return after accomplishing my mission.' He assured her, 'Trust me, Gowru will be very happy.' A highly agitated Subadhramma voiced her concerns: 'But Mahaswami, by crossing the seas you too will break your caste. What will become of us?'

Veerarajendra comforted his wife: 'Our son-in-law Jung Bahadur purified himself by bathing in the holy Ganga. I too will do the same.'

From Fatehgarh, Dr Login and Lena Login closely followed the education and grooming of Princess Gowramma. The couple had long discussions in private, regarding the prospect of a grand alliance between the 'saved souls' of the maharaja of Punjab and the princess from Coorg. They relished the thought of a large number of Indian rulers converting to Christianity, and how they in turn would influence their subjects to discard their superstition-filled religion. A Christian India would be a formidable ally of the British.

Major W.M. Stewart, the British agent in overall charge of many other exiled Indian royalties in Benares and nearby areas, had informed the Logins that Gowramma was an attractive and intelligent girl. He also informed them that the princess's late mother belonged to a local community in Coorg believed to be of Circassian descent. With her frequent interactions with the British, the Princess had also acquired all the desirable Western attitudes and manners.

However, Dalhousie remained apprehensive about Veerarajendra's proposed trip. He was sure that people in England would get carried away and make too much of Veerarajendra and his daughter. In the process, he feared the father and daughter would acquire false airs about themselves. He was not happy about Queen Victoria meeting indolent eastern rulers. He kept telling his close friends that this would turn out to be a huge mistake. Dalhousie was worried how the deposed Indian royalties would behave after their return to India. He wanted no problems in keeping them subservient to the government of India.

Finally, in mid-December 1851, Veerarajendra, accompanied by Gowramma, Mudduveeramma, Siddaveeramma, Seetharamayya, Munshi Shantamalla, and the two servants, started his journey. Seetharamayya had packed condiments required for a year to prepare the raja's favourite dishes. They had to first reach Calcutta from where they would embark on their journey. The departure from Coorg Nest was highly emotional. All the wives, children and other members wailed as the palanquins carrying Veerarajendra, Gowramma and others commenced their strenuous journey. There were great apprehensions that this could be the last time that they would be seeing one another. Subadhramma held Gowramma for a long time, and both shed copious tears in each other's arms. Major and Mrs Drummonds followed the convoy in their palanquin. Prior to the raja of Coorg leaving Benares, Major Stewart made sure Veerarajendra paid the cost of the voyage of the Drummonds along with salary for one year—an amount of 1376 pound sterling.

Veerarajendra's luggage included a heavy rosewood box reinforced with brass trimmings, which he kept close to him. He had packed the strong box with gold and silver coins, precious stones and jewellery for any unforeseen expenses in London. In addition, he, Gowramma, and the two women wore expensive jewellery. The party reached Patna on Christmas-eve. They halted there for a week for the Drummonds to celebrate Christmas.

Gowramma enthusiastically took part in the mid-night mass and the sermon. The Drummonds explained how the worldwide tradition of decorating a Christmas tree had been popularised by Queen Victoria and Prince Albert.

While Veerarajendra and his entourage were on their way to Calcutta, Dalhousie had been on an extended tour. After having spent a month at Simla, he was on his way back to Calcutta. The governor-general and his wife reached Fatehgarh in time to spend Christmas in the company of the thirteen-year-old Maharaja Duleep Singh and the residents at Fatehgarh Park. Dr Login and Lena Login took great effort to celebrate the visit of Lord Dalhousie and Lady Susan Dalhousie. The large Christian community took part in singing carols and hymns. Lena Login arranged for a Christmas tree to be placed in Duleep Singh's mansion. It was brightly festooned with gifts for every Christian dweller at Fatehgarh Park. Duleep Singh, along with Tommy Scott, Robbie Carshore and nephew Sahdev Singh, rushed around helping in all the preparations. The Logins' youngest son, Harry, was just a few months old, and Lena Login needed all the assistance from the youngsters. When Lord Dalhousie heard that Sir Henry Lawrence was godfather to young Harry, he demanded that he be given the privilege of being the godfather to the next child of the Logins.

Lord and Lady Dalhousie reached Fatehgarh Park in time for the Christmas-eve celebrations. After attending the mid-night mass, the Dalhousies retired to the governor-general's well-appointed tent that had been pitched within the estate. The following day the important guests sat down for a sumptuous Christmas lunch. Lord Dalhousie was seeing Duleep Singh after their first momentous meeting in November 1849 at Lahore when the young maharaja was eleven years old. Though he had spoken derogatorily about Duleep Singh and his mother Jindan Kaur in private, he now showed great kindness towards the young maharaja whom he had disdainfully dethroned. The decision of Duleep Singh to embrace Christianity had certainly influenced the obdurate and autocratic Dalhousie to soften his stand. He now took care to address Duleep Singh with the title the boy was permitted to use—'Maharaja'.

During the formal Christmas lunch, Lord Dalhousie sat next to Duleep Singh. He engaged the maharaja in some serious discussions about his education and training. Dalhousie found Duleep Singh to be intelligent and was impressed by his resolve to learn more about Western civilisation. After lunch, the governor general and the maharaja went for a walk within the confines of Fatehgarh Park; to any onlooker they must have appeared like father and son. It was hard to reconcile to the fact that this fatherly gentleman was the one who had deprived Duleep Singh of his vast and prosperous kingdom, including the famed Koh-i-noor diamond.

Before arriving at Fatehgarh, Lord Dalhousie had been busy inspecting two of his pet projects—the ambitious Ganges Canal and the Engineering College at Roorke. He and his wife had been on the move for the last few months. The travelling and camp life had also affected Lady Susan Dalhousie. The sojourn at Fatehgarh was a welcome break. On Dr Login's suggestion, Duleep Singh invited the governor-general and Lady Dalhousie for dinner at his mansion on 27 December 1851. Lord Dalhousie readily agreed.

During the dinner, Dalhousie made an unexpected request. He all of a sudden asked Duleep Singh, 'Maharaja, I would like a portrait of you to remember you by. If you permit me I will send George Beechey, an excellent artist who lives in Calcutta.

A trifle confused, the boy looked at Dr Login. It was Lena Login who said, 'My Lord, that would be an excellent idea. A painting of the maharaja in his regal attire would make an impressive portrait indeed.'

In his private conversation with the Logins, Dalhousie discussed about the possibilities of an alliance between the princess from Coorg and the maharaja of Punjab. Dalhousie told the Logins, 'The raja of Coorg, and his daughter Gowramma are on their way to Calcutta as we speak now. They will board a steamship there, which will take them to Egypt. From Port Suez they will travel by land to Alexandria to board another ship to England. I only pray they behave themselves once on British soil.' Dalhousie was all praise for Princess Gowramma whom he had met during his visits to Benares. He once again lamented the fate of her sister, the stunningly beautiful Princess Gangamma, who had been married off to Jung Bahadur.

During their discussion, Dalhousie noted that Duleep Singh needed more training to smoothen his rough edges. He observed that the maharaja was over-weight and needed more physical activities. He advised Login: 'John, the boy needs to shed some fat. He needs to curtail the tendency to overeat, especially those syrupy Indian sweets.'

George Beechey, the son of a well-known painter in London, was the court painter in the royal household of Oudh. Beechey arrived at Fatehgarh Park in February 1852 on Lord Dalhousie's instructions, and commenced painting the portrait of the teenaged, chubby-faced maharaja. Duleep Singh had several sittings for the portrait, dressed in his ceremonial attire complete with several strands of necklaces and an elaborate bejewelled head-dress. Duleep Singh wore his favourite diamond encrusted pendant with a miniature of Queen Victoria, which was a present from Lord Auckland to his father Maharaja Ranjit Singh. It took a few months for the finished painting to reach Lord Dalhousie at Calcutta. Dalhousie sent a letter full of platitudes to Duleep Singh:

> At last after a long delay upon the river, Your Highness's portrait has arrived. It is in excellent condition, not at all injured by the weather. It is really very much like you and does great credit to Mr Beechey as an artist. Your Highness has really done me a great favour in offering me the likeness of yourself. If it pleases God that I shall live till I am old, I shall look upon it with strong feelings long after my connection with this country shall have been dissolved and always with a renewal of interest which I feel in yourself and in everything belonging to your fate and fortunes.

The entourage of Veerarajendra took about 60 days to cover the nearly 500 miles from Benares to Calcutta, with several halts on the way. The stately colonial buildings in Calcutta, the imperial capital of the British, left them duly impressed. River Hoogly was crowded with boats and ships. The entire city was humming with numerous activities.

Their ship, which was scheduled to leave in February, was delayed due to on-going repairs. After a wait of nearly a month, their vessel set sail from the bustling port of Calcutta on 20 March 1852. The ship moved slowly along the Sunderbans, where the Drummonds told them to look out for tigers in the thick mangroves.

Several ship at the port were being loaded with cotton, indigo, jute, silk and spices by hundreds of sweaty labourers. Veerarajendra and Gowramma stood on the deck of the steamship, awestruck as they entered Bay of Bengal. The reverberating sound of the steam-horn scared away flocks of birds nearby. While the fifty-year-old Veerarajendra was pensive, Gowramma jumped up and down, clapping her hands in joy.

The weather was ideal for the voyage. After about ten days of leisurely sailing, the ship reached Madras port where more passengers boarded and some goods were loaded. They were not permitted to leave the ship during the two days' halt at Madras. Veerarajendra tried to explain to Gowramma, 'My dove, our kingdom Kodagu is about a month's journey from here. On horseback, it could be covered in even less time. I would do anything to go back to my homeland. I miss the place terribly.' Gowru had only heard of Kodagu from her father and her stepmothers. She was not born there, had never set foot on the land of her ancestors, and had no attachment for the place. She was excited at the prospect of seeing London. Her knowledge of London was anyway far more than that of Coorg, which her father insisted on referring as Kodagu.

During the voyage, Drummonds read books by Charles Dickens to Gowru. But she was especially fascinated by Gulliver's Travels, which she tried to read herself, albeit with a lot of difficulty.

The next stopover was at Colombo port. The ship anchored there for about a week, to be serviced and loaded with coal, fresh water and provisions. While the Drummonds disembarked to meet some of their friends in Colombo, Veerarajendra, Gowramma and their companions had to stay on board. Gowramma pleaded, 'Let me too come with you.' The Drummonds, however, were firm and forbade them. Nonetheless, it was a welcome break especially for Mudduveeramma and Siddaveeramma who were much weakened by seasickness. Consignments of various spices, for which Ceylon was well known, were loaded on to the ship.

Also loaded were 34 bags of coffee. Some of the passengers who boarded the ship were planters who grew tea, coffee, cardamom, pepper and other spices in the island. Veerarajendra was told by the British planters about their plans to move to his erstwhile kingdom, which was ideal for cultivation of coffee and spices. 'My father and I have been growing cardamom since early 1800s. In fact, I had leased land to some of the Moplas from Kerala to grow coffee in my kingdom,' the raja reminisced.

The ship set sail by the first week of April, and their route took them close to the east coast of Africa. The vessel made two more stops before entering the Gulf of Aden. The ship finally anchored at the Port of Suez, where all the passengers had to disembark. The on-going journey would be through land. There was a brief halt at Cairo, where the Drummonds took Veerarajendra and Gowramma on a hurried tour of the busy city. Horse carriages were hired to travel from Cairo to Alexandria. Separate carts were needed to transport the raja's and his family's luggage. They reached the port city of Alexandria, where they boarded the SS Euxine belonging to the Peninsular and Oriental Steam Navigation Company. On 20 April 1852, the SS Euxine set sail from Alexandria navigated by Captain E. Cooper.

It was smooth sailing from Alexandria. The SS Euxine docked at Malta and then at Gibraltar. Captain Cooper invited each family on board by turns to a meal with him in his cabin. Veerarajendra, Gowramma and the Drummonds were his guests for dinner while they were crossing the Atlantic Ocean. The raja did not allow the two women in his entourage to be seen in public. They had to cover their faces whenever they came out of their rooms.

The temperature dropped as they moved northwards. Mudduveeramma and Siddaveeramma were miserable with seasickness and the cold weather made them even worse. Gowramma spent most of her time with the Drummonds. They familiarised her with English literature, including stories from some of the plays of Shakespeare. There were daily classes on the scriptures. Veerarajendra was a little worried to find his daughter preferring the company of the Drummonds. Gowramma was moving away not only from her country but also from her family. Subadhramma and Gangamma were the only members of her vast family that she missed.

On 5 May 1852, the SS Euxine docked at the port of Southampton with 129 passengers on board. On disembarking, the passengers presented Captain E. Cooper with a flattering testimonial of their opinion of his 'skill as a seaman, his courteous behaviour, and attention as commander of the ship.'

Arrangements had been made for Veerarajendra, Gowramma and the Drummonds to take the train the following day to London. The rest of the party stayed behind until accommodation could be found for them in London. During the train journey, Veerarajendra and Gowramma were shaken to the core at the amazing speed of the train. 'We are now covering 30 miles every hour!' Major Drummond explained to the incredulous raja and his daughter. Veerarajendra and Gowramma were spellbound at the magnitude of the cities, factories and farms they sped past. Gowramma, who had in the course of her lessons seen paintings of some of the famous structures, was able to identify them. The Drummonds pointed out the important landmarks of London. Gowramma felt as if she was in a fairyland. *The Times, London* had sent photographers and reporters to cover the arrival of the raja and his daughter. The following news was carried in their evening issue dated 8 May 1852:

The Rajah and his daughter left Southampton, with Major Drummond and his family, by an early train on Thursday morning, to take lodging at Mivart's Hotel for the Rajah, previous to his taking a private residence. The Rajah and the Major returned to Southampton in the afternoon, and the whole of his family and suite proceeded to London by the 7 PM train. The Rajah's wives left Euxine, completely veiled… and were conveyed to Radley's Hotel in a closed carriage. They were met at the door of the hotel by the Rajah and one of his principal attendants, who both held umbrellas over the heads of the ladies as they alighted. As soon as they left the carriage they took the umbrellas themselves, and completely screened themselves from view. During the process of their alighting from the carriage, however, a glimpse of one of them was obtained, and it was noticed that the lady had a thin gauze veil over her face and fine black eyes. The Rajah was exceedingly anxious that no one should observe the ladies, and appeared agitated until they were safely in their apartment. His agitation was so great when he had conducted them upstairs that he could not open the door of the apartment, and imagining it was locked, he requested that the gas should be extinguished in the passage where they were standing, which was immediately done. The Prince has given up his caste. He is a pensioner of the East India Company and has been residing at Benares on an allowance of 12,000-pound sterling a year. Yesterday the Rajah's six servants, who, by his desire, observed most strictly the rules of their caste, had eight pounds of food allowed them, which consisted of rice, onion and greens, which they cooked and ate in the open air at the back of the hotel. They have but one meal a day, and their drink is water. They are, in fact, Oriental vegetarians and teetotallers. At night, they slept in the passages and under tables in the hotel.

(There are some inaccuracies in the above report. Veerarajendra received an annual allowance of 6,000-pound sterling equivalent to 60,000 rupees. The raja had not given up his caste, but was sympathetic to Christianity.)

The Board of Directors of the East India Company had organised a warm welcome for the ex-raja of Coorg and his daughter. Veerarajendra was the first deposed Indian sovereign ruler, and Gowramma the first princess from India, to visit England. One of the Company's representatives was at the station to meet the raja and his entourage. Horse carriages were arranged to take Veerarajendra and Gowramma to their temporary place of residence at the fashionable Mivart's Hotel in the centre of London. Major and Mrs Drummonds were met by their two young daughters and relatives. It was a joyous homecoming for them after many years in India. The rest of the raja's party reached London later to take their residence at the nearby less expensive Radley's Hotel.

It took a week for Veerarajendra, Mudduveeramma, Siddaveeramma and the servants to recover from the fatigue of the long voyage. Gowramma, on the other hand, was full of energy, and eager to go out to explore the great city. She anxiously looked forward to the Drummonds to take her on a tour of London. Having set up a temporary kitchen, Seetharamayya cooked the raja's favourite dishes with the help of the two servants.

A few days later, there was a formal welcome for Veerarajendra and Gowramma by the Directors of the East India Company. The press was informed of the presence of the Indian royalty in London. The reporters were impressed that the young princess could converse quite well in English.

The arrival in London of the raja of Coorg and his daughter was brought to the notice of Queen Victoria and Prince Albert. The thirty-three-year-old Queen Victoria was already a mother of seven children, and godmother to many more. Married to Prince Albert, who advised her on the affairs of the state, she had time for family and friends. By then, the British monarchy 'reigned, not ruled' in England. It was a ceremonial post and they could only give their counsel to the democratically elected government. Nonetheless, Queen Victoria took personal interest in the lives of those close to her. With her emphasis on family values, concern for the poor, emphasis on industrialisation and steps to improve the living standards of the common man, she won the hearts of the poor and middle class in England. The story of Princess Gowramma of Coorg, from one of the smallest provinces of the British colony in India, appealed immensely to the queen and her consort.

5

GROOMING OF THE CHRISTIAN PRINCESS

*T*WO WEEKS AFTER their arrival in London, Major and Mrs Drummond came to meet Veerarajendra at the Mivart's Hotel to inform him that a house, 23, Onslow Square, Brompton, had been arranged in the city for him and his family. Munshi Shantamalla then settled on an auspicious date and time for the raja to shift to his new residence. On the appointed date, the Drummonds brought horse carriages to transport the raja and his family to their new home, where a pooja was performed, Mudduveeramma boiled the traditional pot of milk and both the women sprinkled water from the Ganges that they had carried from India in all the rooms. The women were especially delighted at shifting to their new home as they could hope for much more privacy than at the Radley's Hotel.

Gowramma stayed close to the Drummonds in the hope that they would take her on an excursion of London, as promised during their sea voyage. But first there were many arrangements to be made. Major Drummond had a message for Veerarajendra from the Directors of the East India Company. They wanted the raja to write a formal letter to the queen, requesting Her Majesty to accept his dear daughter Gowramma into the Christian fold. The Drummonds stayed at Mivart's Hotel at Veerarajendra's expense whenever they came to London. They helped the raja draft the letter to the queen. Mrs Drummond comforted a disappointed Gowramma, 'Dear Gowru, you'll have to stay with your father till a communication is received from the queen.' They left a book of fairy tales by the Brothers Grimm, and a painting set to keep her occupied. The Company had provided two English attendants to help Veerarajendra with security, and for arranging household provisions, and so forth.

The directors of the East India Company invited Veerarajendra and Gowramma along with the Drummonds for lunch where a number of influential people were also present. Many curious Londoners belonging to high society were keen to meet the first Indian raja to visit England. There were quite a few invitations for the raja and his daughter to visit English homes. On a recommendation from the Board of Control, Veerarajendra employed one John James Birkett as his personal secretary to help him in his interaction with others in London.

In the meantime, Veerarajendra requested an audience with the queen. The raja and his daughter were elated when they were invited to meet the queen and Prince Albert at Buckingham

Palace on 17 May 1852. Munshi Shantamalla dressed in his best was present as an attendant. John C. Harries, the president of the Board of Control for the Affairs of India, escorted Veerarajendra and Princess Gowramma. Veerarajendra knelt respectfully before the Sovereign and gifted a pendant made of tiger claws to the queen and an ornate Coorg knife—*peechekatti*—to Prince Albert. Queen Victoria was pleased with the little eastern-Princess who was impeccable in her manners, though a little nervous. The letter from Veerarajendra to the queen was handed over to her secretary.

Queen Victoria was prompt in her response. A dispatch from the Right Honourable J.C. Harries of the Board of Control of East India Company, dated 7 June 1852, was delivered to Veerarajendra in which it was conveyed that the queen was highly appreciative of the raja's intentions of raising his daughter according to the principles of Christianity. The queen let it be known that she would confer with the archbishop of Canterbury on the subject, and would appoint a time under His Grace's advice for the performance of the ceremony of baptism. Veerarajendra and Gowramma were overwhelmed when told that 'Her Majesty is graciously pleased to signify her intentions of being present, and of standing sponsor to the young princess.'

Major and Mrs Drummonds were informed of the development, and were requested to come to London immediately to prepare Gowramma for the rituals involved in the baptism. Princess Gowramma, who had been somewhat depressed till then, was delighted when the Drummond couple arrived at 23, Onslow Square. She enthusiastically learnt all that the Drummonds had to teach her about the baptism ritual. Veerarajendra too had to learn the formalities and protocol required to be observed when formally presented to the queen and Prince Albert.

On 28 June 1852, the Lord Chamberlain formally invited Veerarajendra on instructions from the queen:

'Lord Chamberlain is commanded by Her Majesty to invite His Highness the Prince Veer Rajunder Wadeer to attend the christening of his daughter in the chapel at Buckingham Palace on Wednesday next, the 30 instant, at a quarter before one o' clock.'

Accordingly, the ceremony took place on 30 June 1852 and was attended by the family members of the queen and quite a few prominent members of the British society, including senior officials of the East India Company. The queen and her prince consort found the young princess beautiful, poised and well mannered. Queen Victoria was fascinated with the girl's expressive dark brown doe eyes. They were aware that the girl had lost her mother soon after she was born. In Gowramma, the royal couple saw a god-sent opportunity to groom a member of the Indian royal family in Western thought. Gowramma was dressed in a laced white double-skirt and held a bouquet of flowers in her hands. In spite of the apprehensions of the Drummonds, Veerarajendra too conducted himself admirably. He wore his jaunty royal attire amply embellished with expensive jewels. The glittering gems on his person attracted the attention of the guests.

His Grace, the archbishop of Canterbury, John Bird Sumner, conducted the baptism ritual, accepting Gowramma as a member of the Church of England. He sprinkled holy water from River Jordan on the Indian princess and uttered the Trinitarian invocation, 'I baptise you: In the name of the Father, and of the Son, and of the Holy Spirit.' Queen Victoria was the most important sponsor of the princess. Her Majesty amazed everyone by announcing herself as the godmother of Princess Gowramma. There was further surprise when she declared, 'I would like the newly baptised Princess from Coorg, my goddaughter, to be christened Victoria Gowramma.' The other notables who were sponsors at the baptism were Viscountess Hardinge, wife of Viscount Hardinge, the former governor-general of India, Sir James Weir-Hogg, chairman, East India Company and Mrs Drummond.

The baptism of Princess Gowramma was carried out under an agreement between Veerarajendra, the raja of Coorg, and the Board of Control and Board of Directors of the East India Company. By this agreement, the Princess was placed under the protection of Her Majesty, the queen, to be educated in the principles of the Church of England. The queen entrusted Princess Victoria Gowramma to the care of Major and Mrs Drummond with instructions to teach the little Princess a more thorough knowledge of the Bible, and provide her a sound British education.

After the baptism ritual, princess Victoria Gowramma knelt deferentially in front of Queen Victoria and kissed her godmother's hand. The queen held Gowramma's hand and said, 'I congratulate you Victoria Gowramma, on your baptism and acceptance into the Church of England.' The queen then presented Gowramma a beautiful leather-bound copy of the Holy Bible embellished with gold-plated trimmings, studs and a clasp. The queen autographed the book, and wrote the following message:

To,

Victoria Gauramma,

on the day of her Baptism,

from

her very affectionate

Godmother & well-wisher

Victoria R

Buckingham Palace

30 June 1852

The queen announced the arrangement of 400 rupees per month to be set aside from the revenue of Coorg for the education and maintenance of Princess Victoria Gowramma. The Coorg princess was thus the first member from an Indian royal family to be taken under the wings of the queen. She was the first Indian princess to leave her religion and embrace Christianity. The English society was even more impressed by the fact that her Hindu father, a ruler dethroned by the British, had willingly encouraged his daughter to embark on this unusual yet noble journey.

Veerarajendra was ecstatic at the spectacular ceremony and the commitment of the queen. He was jubilant at the turn of events. It was far more than what he had expected. He made an emotional statement, which was translated to English by Major James Drummond:

> My dearest daughter – Endeavour to gain every day more and more the grace, and to merit the love and kindness of Her most gracious Majesty, the Queen; that thereby all Europe, India, and the rest of the world, may hear and be pleased with your good conduct and fame. May heaven bless you, and keep you always under its divine protection and special care! This is my advice to you, my dearest daughter, and my most earnest prayer to the Almighty in your behalf.

With these words, he ceremoniously handed over his daughter to Her Majesty's charge, as other members of the royal family—Prince Albert, the prince of Wales, the Princess Royal and Princess Alice witnessed the ceremony. All the leading newspapers in London carried this astonishing story. The queen and the British society anticipated it to be an exciting boost for the enlightening message of Christ spreading in the heathen colony. It was surmised that for the successful proselytisation of the vast subcontinent, it was necessary to attract the upper classes of caste-ridden Indian society to the teachings of Jesus Christ. *The Times, London* carried this 'Court Circular' in their issue dated 1 July 1852:

COURT CIRCULAR.

The Queen will hold a Privy Council this afternoon at Buckingham Palace. Summonses were issued yesterday from the Privy Council-office to the Ministers and officers of State.

The ceremony of the baptism of the Princess Gauromma, daughter of his Highness Prince Vere Rejunder, ex-Rajah of Coorg, took place at 1 o'clock yesterday afternoon, in the Private Chapel of Buckingham Palace.

The ceremony was performed by the Archbishop of Canterbury, assisted by the Rev. Lord Wriothesley Russell, Deputy-Clerk of the Closet in Waiting, and the Hon. and Rev. Gerald Wellesley, Domestic Chaplain to Her Majesty.

Her Majesty the Queen was pleased to stand sponsor. The other sponsors were the Viscountess Hardinge, Mrs. Drummond, and Sir James Weir Hogg, Bart., Chairman of the East India Company. The Princess was named by Her Majesty "Victoria."

His Royal Highness Prince Albert, their Royal Highnesses the Prince of Wales, the Princess Royal, Prince Alfred, and the Princess Alice, and his Highness Prince Vere Rajunder, were present at the ceremony.

Her Majesty was attended by the Duchess of Atholl, Mistress of the Robes, the Viscountess Canning, Lady in Waiting, Lady Caroline Barrington, the Hon. Caroline Cavendish, and the Hon. Flora Macdonald, Maids of Honour in Waiting, the Marquis of Exeter, Lord Chamberlain, Lord Byron, Lord in Waiting, Colonel the Hon. C. B. Phipps, Sir Frederick Stovin, Groom in Waiting, Major-General Buckley, Equerry in Waiting, and Lieutenant-Colonel Biddulph, Master of the Household.

The Marquis of Abercorn, Groom of the Stole, and Colonel Bouverie, Equerry in Waiting, were in attendance on the Prince.

The Viscount Hardinge, the Right Hon. John C. Herries, President of the Board of Control for the Affairs of India, and Major Drummond, 3d Bengal Light Cavalry, were also honoured with invitations to attend the ceremony.

> After the christening the distinguished circle were con-
> ducted to the Dinner-room, where luncheon was served.
>   Prince Vere Rajunder and the Princess Gauromma, at-
> tended by their suite, left the Palace at 20 minutes past
> 2 o'clock.

Young Gowramma was mesmerised to find herself in the company of the the British royalty. The formal luncheon at the Palace hosted in her honour soon after the ceremony was like a dream. The queen advised Gowramma to concentrate on her education under the guidance of Mrs Drummond: 'I want you to be well versed in English literature, culture, history and above all, the words in the Holy Bible. We will have a rite of confirmation once we are sure you are well prepared. You will then be ready to be formally presented to the English society.'

The same day, later in the afternoon, the newly-baptised Princess Victoria Gowramma and her father were invited to be present at the House of Lords where the queen addressed the members of the upper house. Both father and daughter attracted great deal of attention with their resplendent attire. The newspapers reported Veerarajendra wearing 'barbaric' strands of pearls, and heavy jewellery. His daughter was described in yet another news item in *The Times, London* of 1 July 1852 as a bright-eyed, delicate-featured, copper-hued young girl.

Major and Mrs Drummond stayed at Mivart's Hotel for over a month to familiarise Gowramma with London. Gowramma was taken to all the important places in the metropolis. She found the hustle and bustle of the city most exhilarating. The Drummonds took her to Westminster Abbey, the Tower of London, Saint Paul's Cathedral, Saint George's Chapel and other places of interest. The place she liked the most was Madame Tussaud's wax museum. Mrs Drummond explained to Gowramma about Marie Tussaud the architect of the museum, and that it was just two years ago that she had died.

Gowramma would narrate to her father about all the fascinating places she had visited with the Drummonds. Though happy to see his daughter enjoying herself, Veerarajendra was concerned about the heavy expenses he had to incur because of the Drummonds, who insisted on staying at the expensive Mivart's Hotel even though a suite of rooms was available for them at 23, Onslow Square.

Gowramma bombarded Mrs Drummond with a barrage of questions about London. She was very happy to learn about British history by visiting various historical locations. She did not much like to read on her own, preferring books and stories to be read out to her. The Drummonds found that the girl was not able to concentrate on serious studies and was distracted easily. Her father's excessive doting did not help matters. Finally, they concluded that Gowramma's education could not progress satisfactorily if she stayed with her father. The queen too concurred that the impressionable princess should be removed from the conflicting Hindu influence of her father's household. They found a house in Kew to keep Gowramma away from Veerarajendra, and stop him from meddling in her upbringing.

Back in India, Lord Dalhousie penned his thoughts in a letter dated 24 September 1852, to Dr Login about Veerarajendra, when the doctor brought up the issue of Maharaja Duleep Singh's visit to England:

> ...I have been greatly disgusted with the notoriety they have given the Raja of Coorg in England, though I had carefully provided against it here and had warned them on the subject.

It had been calculated to turn the girl's (Gowramma) head and his too, for he will now be more convinced than ever of his accomplishing his object of marrying her to an English nobleman. Whether he would prefer a Maharaja pucka to a nobleman in prospect, I do not know! Nor do I feel that the Maharaja would do well to arrange any marriage until he has seen the young lady; for as a Christian, he can't get Ranees in duplicate, he may as well see how he likes her first... The little heathen sister whom Jung Bahadur took away with him to Nepal was really very pretty. The orthodox one is not nearly as good-looking!...

The news of Veerarajendra's and his daughter Gowramma's travel to England and the young princess having converted to Christianity reached Coorg several months after the event. It took nearly a year for it to trickle down to some of the local leaders. When the raja's friend Alamanda Somayya heard the news, he realised that his prophesy about Princess Gowramma crossing the seas had come true! He too, by then, had decided to embrace Christianity and had sought the help of the German Protestant priest, Reverend Herman Moegling.

Reverend Moegling, who had successfully established a Christian mission in Mangalore, had moved to Coorg in the hope of spreading the words of Jesus Christ amongst the pagan Coorgs. Somayya was baptised in January 1853, and was given the name Stephanous Somayya. Somayya was the first in Coorg to embrace Christianity, and he became an important assistant to Reverend Moegling in his evangelic movement in Coorg. However, the general populace in Coorg was not much influenced by the news of Veerarajendra and his daughter Gowramma. Having seen two decades of British administration, the people of Coorg were happier than they were during the reign of Veerarajendra.

The Coorgs remained fiercely loyal to their religious beliefs and form of worship, which predominantly was reverence for ancestors and nature. However, since the advent of the Haleri rajas, Hinduism also came to be accepted and followed by the Coorgs. While they welcomed many reforms introduced by the British government including educational institutions run by the missionaries, the people of Coorg found no *raison d'être* to change their form of worship. On the other hand, Stephanous Somayya's conversion was considered an isolated case; his primary need to embrace Christianity seen more as a solution to his dire financial problems.

Reverend Moegling was very happy on hearing about Princess Gowramma's conversion. He observed:

A child of this house (the raja's family) has found her way into the Church of Christ; and Queen Victoria, sovereign of the greatest empire of the world, has not been ashamed to bestow her name and affection upon a daughter of the last of the Haleri Rajahs. Auspicious omen for Coorg! O give thanks unto to the Lord, for he is good; for his mercy endureth for ever!

With his daughter having settled well to her new life, Veerarajendra thought the time was ripe for him to take up the issue of filing a legal claim on the investments made by his uncle with the British East India Company way back in 1810. On instructions from Dr Jeaffreson, three legal experts, Sir Roundell Palmer, Mr Leith and Mr Schomberg, visited the raja to discuss the case. Veerarajendra was told that his prospects were good for winning the suit soon to be filed at Chancery Court.

However, the directors of the East India Company were affronted when the raja·of Coorg filed a legal case against the Company. In retaliation, they asked Veerarajendra and his companions to return to Benares since they had already stayed beyond the permitted one year in England. In March 1853, Veerarajendra had applied for an extension of his stay citing poor health, and the necessity for his presence in England to see his minor daughter well settled. The Court of Directors not only rejected the raja's request, but also stopped payment of his pension with effect from 20 March 1853. However, his lawyers succeeded in preventing him from being shipped back to India, since his case was still pending at the Chancery Court. Veerarajendra had to fall back on his reserve of gold and silver coins to maintain his establishment.

The Drummonds wanted to take their ward away from London to shield her from what they referred to as 'the undesirable environment' in her father's residence. After a few months at Kew, the Drummonds obtained permission from the queen to take Gowramma to Scotland so that she could be brought up along with their two daughters. The India Office welcomed this move since they now regarded the raja as an 'old reprobate'. Mudduveeramma, Siddaveeramma and their Brahmin cook performed regular poojas in the house and the Drummonds feared these rituals would create confusion in the mind of the young princess during her visits to meet her father.

The prospect of travelling to Scotland by rail excited Gowramma. During the train journey, she sat glued to the window, gazing at the countryside they were passing through. Unlike her earlier experience, she enjoyed the great speed at which they were travelling.

The Drummonds moved to a house in a secluded farm near Edinburgh where their two daughters, both younger to Gowramma, joined them. The Drummonds set strict study schedules for the three girls. Gowramma, not accustomed to being regimented, disliked the discipline. As days passed, she started getting increasingly recalcitrant. Mrs Drummond pointed to a pile of books and tried to impress upon the princess, 'Her Majesty wants me to teach you all there is to learn from these books. Princess, you will have to concentrate and master these subjects. Your confirmation will depend on how well you imbibe knowledge in various subjects.' In the course of a few months the Drummond girls, though younger, were far ahead in their studies than Gowramma. This depressed and disheartened the princess further. She sulked and would cheer up only when taken out to the city. She immensely enjoyed the picnics arranged in the country, where she would actively participate in all the preparations. On these occasions, she helped the Drummonds much more than their daughters. Another activity that caught her fancy was ballroom dancing, which was taught to the three girls by Mrs Drummond.

Nearly a year passed by. Gowramma neither showed any great interest in her studies nor in music or painting. The dazzling exposure to the British royalty had made her crave for more attention. She was not particularly homesick, and when the Drummonds took her to visit her father, Gowramma found she had little in common with her family. She found it difficult to converse with them having lost touch with her own language. However, she longed for the love and affection of a mother. She had no one to confide into. She was twelve years old and undergoing several changes. Though Mrs Drummond was kind to Gowramma, she could not provide the motherly support that the young girl desperately yearned.

The case filed against the East India Company on behalf of the raja of Coorg created quite a stir in the British society. There were several write-ups in the newspapers; the liberals in the Whigs party sympathised with the Indian royalty. When a month later, Lord Dalhousie received the news in India of the legal case filed by Veerarajendra, he reacted angrily towards the Board of Directors for not heeding his advice. He had stoutly opposed Veerarajendra's visit to England. On the other hand, Major Evans Bell who relentlessly exposed the arrogance and avarice of officers of the British East India Company, hailed this move by the raja of Coorg as a step in the right direction. He wanted the justice system, which the British prided themselves in, to be applicable equitably. Major Evans predicted more legal suits against the Company by deposed rulers in the months ahead.

During the session of the House of Commons on 26 June 1853, one of the prominent members, Mr J.G. Phillimore, rose to introduce a clause in the Government of India Bill. He proposed introduction of queen's judges at competent courts at each Presidency in India, so that any dispute between the government of the British East India Company in India and any native prince, not a subject of British Crown, could be given an impartial hearing. He proposed an additional provision of a final appeal to the Privy Council in England. He went on to say, 'If ever there was a period, when the establishment of such a tribunal was necessary, that time was the present, and if any proof were required one has to refer to the language which was being constantly used by Lord Dalhousie.'

Mr Phillimore lamented that there was no provision for redress of the woes of the Indian princes. He came down heavily on the East India Company, and termed their actions 'obnoxious to all principles of jurisprudence'. Mr Phillimore was specific when he said in the House of Commons, 'There could not be greater instances of cold-blooded cruelty than had been practiced by the Court of Directors towards the rajas of Coorg and Satara.'

However, this proposal did not find favour with the majority conservative members and was voted out 74 to 61.

Meanwhile, not all was well at 23, Onslow Square. Within two years of their stay in London, Munshi Shantamalla wanted to go back to his family in India. Unhappy and depressed, he had taken to drinking, and his behaviour had come under criticism by the Drummonds. When Veerarajendra, who depended on the Munshi a great deal, did not permit him to return, Shantamalla tried to take his own life by jumping from the Westminster Bridge across River Thames. A police officer saved him from drowning in the dirty waters of the river with help from a waterman employed by the Bridge Committee. Found in a highly inebriated condition, Munshi Shantamalla was arrested for attempted suicide and remanded to police custody. Veerarajendra had to appear before the Magistrate on two occasions before his assistant was released. To make matters worse, it was discovered that Shantamalla had contracted a 'loathsome disease'. The raja assured the court that Shantamalla would be treated for his ailment, and paid salary for two months and the expenses of his voyage back to Benares. By the end of Nov 1853, the weary Munshi boarded a ship to return home. The police officer received half-a-sovereign from the raja for his efforts in saving Shantamalla.

To garner public sympathy in his legal battle with the Company, Veerarajendra's lawyers advised him to write a detailed letter to some of the leading newspapers. They were of the view that public opinion would promote further discussions on the subject in the House of Commons. Accordingly, a comprehensive letter was drafted by them on behalf of the raja, and sent to all newspapers. On 17 November 1853, Veerarajendra's letter appeared in The Daily News under the heading, 'A Prince Dethroned by the East India Company'. This letter did evoke some compassion in favour of Veerarajendra and prevented the Company from evicting him from England. Fearing adverse publicity, his pension was grudgingly restored.

Despite Lord Dalhousie's outbursts in private against the raja, and the indifferent attitude of the East India Company, Veerarajendra continued to receive invitations from the queen for various court functions and was accorded appropriate protocol. The raja of Coorg had the privilege of being invited to the thirty-fifth birthday celebration of Queen Victoria at St. James's Palace on 20 May 1854. The reception included all the members of the Royal family, the whole of the Diplomatic Corp, and a galaxy of nobility and gentry, which altogether numbered 1400.

Again, on 9 June 1854, Veerarajendra was a prominent invited at Her Majesty's Levee—a ceremonial reception, held in the afternoons, specifically for high-ranking royalty, diplomats, and visiting dignitaries. The function, intended only for gentlemen, was held in the Throne Room at St. James's Palace. The king of Portugal was the guest of honour.

Veerarajendra made heads turn at every gathering he attended, with his impressive ethnic attire and glittering jewellery. At the Levee, The Times, London reported him wearing two thick gold collars round his neck. While one of them was studded entirely with diamonds, the other had a large emerald encircled by diamonds. He wore a turban, with a magnificent diamond in front. In addition, he had, as further reported in *The Times*, 'barbaric' strands of pearls round his neck.

Her Majesty's invitations to Veerarajendra to attend important court functions made him highly optimistic of achieving his goal of securing the proceeds of the two promissory notes.

6

DULEEP SINGH EMBRACES CHRISTIANITY

$\mathcal{D}$URING THE SPRING of 1852, the Logins were well settled in Fatehgarh with the young and impressionable Maharaja Duleep Singh under their care. Before the brutal onslaught of the north Indian summer, the Logins planned to take a tour of the nearby historic places with their young charge to rekindle the maharaja's interest in learning. Their infant son Harry was now almost a year old, and they too desired an outing for him from the rather secluded life in Fatehgarh Park. After visiting the nearby places of interest, they planned to proceed to Mussoorie, where they would spend the remaining hot summer months.

It was an impressive entourage that finally set out from Fatehgarh Park with elephants, horses, herds of goats and a pack of greyhounds. The journey was undertaken at a leisurely pace, covering ten miles a day, with the party camping in the maharaja's trademark red-and-white-striped tents with silver tent-posts.

The maharaja and his party halted at Agra for a week. From the spot where they had pitched their tents, the white marble monument—the Taj Mahal—was clearly visible. The surreal glow of the mausoleum in the moonlight was a captivating sight indeed! The English community at Agra welcomed the visitors with a grand reception in the maharaja's honour. The fact that Duleep Singh was soon to embrace their religion made them go out of their way to extend an impressive welcome to the maharaja and his companions.

The grounds of the Taj Mahal was taken over to host an elaborate breakfast in honour of Duleep Singh, the Logins, his tutor Walter Guise, friends Tommy and Robbie, nephew Shahzadah Sahdev Singh, Rani Duknu, and the maharaja's English coachman and valet, Thornton. Rani Duknu was the only reluctant guest. She was not happy at her son being exposed to the idiosyncrasies of his uncle. Duleep Singh was overwhelmed by the grandeur of the monument. Colourful marquees had been erected near the grand entrance to the mausoleum. The maharaja wore his royal attire replete with several strands of pearl and diamond necklaces. The oval miniature of Queen Victoria was one of the prominent embellishments around his neck. The English men and women came dressed as they would for the races. His partaking in a meal in the historic edifice with the Europeans was another message to his countrymen that he remained steadfast in his determination to convert to Christianity.

On their way out of Agra, the party visited the grand tomb of Emperor Akbar. Walter Guise gave the boys a brief lesson on Mughal history. However, Duleep Singh was in a playful mood and kept everyone entertained with his pranks. At the great emperor's mausoleum, in his attempts to race up the stairs, one of the strands of his pearls came undone and the pigeon-egg-sized beads were scattered all over the place. His servants and friends had to crawl on all fours to search every nook and cranny to find the precious pearls. The juvenile maharaja burst into hysterical laughter at the discomfiture of his entourage. They then proceeded to Delhi, and on the way Dr Login took the young maharaja to a factory manufacturing printing blocks and typesets. They also made a visit to study the progress of an electric telegraph station, which was scheduled to be commissioned in a few months.

On reaching Delhi, they pitched their tents on the banks of the river Yamuna. Across the river, they could see the imposing Red Fort and the impressive Metcalfe House with its massive marble columns. The mansion, built by the British Agent at Delhi, Sir Thomas Metcalfe, was intended to rival the opulence of Emperor Bahadur Shah Zafar who was confined within the Red Fort. The British Agent was then more powerful than the Mughal Emperor who needed Metcalfe's permission to leave the Red Fort. However, Duleep Singh was more interested in shopping in Delhi than in visiting ancient monuments. The Logins still managed to take their pupil to see the Qutub Minar, Jantar Mantar, Humayun's tomb and Chandni Chowk. At Chandni Chowk, the young maharaja was happy to see all the shops with their colourful array of goods. He avidly shopped for jewellery to add to his already impressive collection. Rani Duknu too bought jewellery for herself and her son Sahdev Singh, who she was sure, would be the next maharaja of Punjab.

After Delhi, they proceeded to Roorke, where they visited the Ganges Canal Works, one of the pet projects of Lord Dalhousie, and about which the governor-general had spoken at length to them during his visit to Fatehgarh over Christmas. The project, already six years in the making, was scheduled to be completed by 1854. It was described to the young maharaja how the canal was intended to be the largest in the world at that time. Parts of the canal had already been commissioned, and on completion it would irrigate about 1,470,000 acres of land. Dr Login recalled Lord Dalhousie's words, 'When fully commissioned, no single canal in Europe would be half in magnitude of this great undertaking in India.' Dalhousie had paid glowing tributes to Colonel Proby Cautley, the engineer in charge of designing and building the canal.

On reaching Haridwar, Duleep Singh expressed his desire to see the religious ceremonies being conducted at the ghats. There were a large number of pilgrims from Punjab, and the authorities at Haridwar were apprehensive about the reaction of the crowd on seeing the maharaja. The main party was therefore sent in a different direction as a decoy, and Duleep Singh made a quick visit to the bathing ghats on his elephant. As he was leaving, some of his former subjects from Punjab recognised him and loudly hailed and cheered him. Duleep Singh was highly pleased at the response.

A week later, they reached the cool climes of Mussoorie. It took them a couple of days to get over the fatigue of travelling. Dr Login made it clear to the boys right at the outset that during their stay in Mussoorie, the focus would be on learning, hobbies, sports, and games.

Dr Login and Walter Guise set strict routines for the maharaja and his friends. Local experts were invited to teach the boys diverse subjects such as astronomy, biology, zoology, flora and fauna of the Himalayas, habits of bees, etc., besides the English language. During their free time, they were coached in archery, cricket and music. The maharaja, however, could not resist indulging in falconry during his spare time. Duleep Singh showed great promise in music and impressed his music teacher, Mr Hunter. His favourite instruments were the flute and the cornopean. Maharaja Duleep Singh, along with his nephew Sahdev, and Robbie Carshore and Tommy Scott, entertained the locals by forming a band and playing at the Mall.

Duleep Singh made friends with the children of some of the British officers stationed at Mussoorie, especially the two teenage sons of an army officer, Major Boileau, who had just arrived from England. Dr Login wrote to Dalhousie: 'The Boileau boys are very intelligent lads of fifteen and sixteen, who appear to have been carefully educated, and are very diligent and attentive to their Urdu studies. I have little doubt that their example will be in every way beneficial to His Highness.' Dr Login also informed Dalhousie of the fact that with all the outdoor activities, the maharaja had lost most of his puppy fat, and now appeared trim and handsome.

Around August 1852, Maharaja Duleep Singh read the news of Princess Gowramma's baptism, more than a month after the event was published in *The Times* and the *Illustrated London News*. He was an avid reader of the newspapers that arrived at regular intervals from London. He had many questions to ask the Logins and his tutor Walter Guise. Duleep Singh was impressed that Queen Victoria had taken Gowramma under her care and stood sponsor at her baptism. He read with great interest about the elaborate ceremony of the princess receiving the sacrament of baptism from the archbishop and the queen giving Gowramma the exalted name 'Victoria'. Duleep Singh found the young princess to be quite attractive from the photographs published in the *Illustrated London News*.

After reading about Princess Gowramma, Duleep Singh was rather pensive for a while and about a week later, he confided in Dr Login: 'Princess Victoria Gowramma seems suitable as a wife for me for more than one reason. It may be a good idea to negotiate with her father, the raja of Coorg, a marriage alliance between us.' Dr Login and his wife were very pleased that the proposal about which they had, in fact, been contemplating in private, had been voiced by Duleep Singh himself. The momentous news was conveyed to Lord Dalhousie, who too thought that it was the best possible option for both the Indian royalties.

Lord Dalhousie, however, continued to be cynical of the highly publicised baptism of Princess Gowramma. In his private letter to Sir George Couper, he strongly criticised the queen for bestowing the name 'Victoria' on her. Dalhousie felt that the 'rascally raja of Coorg' and his daughter would regard the sacrament as a Court pageant, which he feared would turn their heads. He informed Dr Login that this sort of '*tamasha*' should be avoided in Duleep Singh's case. He wrote to Dr Login 'If Duleep Singh is to go to England, let him be quietly baptised before he goes, and by his own name of Duleep Singh. Indeed, I am prepared to advise him being baptised now, as soon as his minister can declare that he is sufficiently instructed, and is willing to be baptised at all. He is quite old enough to take the obligations directly upon himself, to be baptised without the intervention of godfathers and godmothers.'

Four months had passed since their arrival at Mussoorie, and the Login couple felt that the young maharaja was sufficiently prepared for baptism. Dr Login went on to urge Dalhousie:

> From all I have seen of the Maharaja's disposition, I am the more satisfied as to the great advantage and stimulus of example in his case. His disposition is naturally indolent, and nothing but his strong good sense, and his desire to be on equality in knowledge and accomplishments with lads of his own age, enables him to overcome the natural slothfulness of his character. It is on this account that I am so anxious that he should be permitted to visit England as he so earnestly desires it, while he is young, and while he can have an opportunity of mixing with lads of his own age, and incur less risk of being spoiled by too great attention.

The stay at Mussoorie was a great success, and all of them were reluctant to leave the hill station and move back to the plains. Both the Boileau boys decided to accompany the maharaja to spend time at Fatehgarh. On popular demand, their music teacher, Mr Hunter, too decided to accompany the entourage to continue his lessons. It took another two months for them to reach Fatehgarh. The Logins tried their best to fit in some studies and educational tours on their way back to Fatehgarh. They constantly tested Duleep Singh's understanding of the Holy Bible.

Ever since Princess Gowramma's much publicised baptism, Duleep Singh was eagerly awaiting his own. He too wished the ceremony to be held in London with pomp and splendour. But Lord Dalhousie had already instructed Dr Login that the baptism of Maharaja Duleep Singh was to be performed in India and that too without any publicity. Moreover, Duleep Singh's religious instructor Reverend Carshore was not convinced that the young maharaja was ready for sacrament. In spite of the Logins and Dalhousie himself wanting the conversion to take place without any delay, Reverend Carshore was categorical that his pupil was not sufficiently instructed. Duleep Singh's preoccupation with hawking, hunting and playing games from the *Boys' Own Book* had come in the way of his religious education. Under the circumstances, the christening ceremony had to be postponed for the following year.

Back in Fatehgarh, Reverend Carshore resumed Duleep Singh's instructions in Christianity and the Scriptures. The Military Chaplain of the station at Fatehgarh, Rev William Jay, too gave lessons in the Gospels for the benefit of the maharaja. By the end of October 1852, the padre was fairly convinced that the maharaja was ready to take the final step to enter the Christian fold.

Dr Login made Duleep Singh write a personal letter to Lord Dalhousie to impress upon the governor-general that he was ready and eager to be baptised. Consequently, Duleep Singh wrote to the governor-general on 6 February 1853:

My dear good Friend,

I think I now sufficiently understand the Christian religion, and the duties to which it binds me, and have a strong desire to be baptized, which I trust, therefore, I may be considered fit for. I remain,

Yours very truly,
Duleep Singh

Dalhousie was much pleased with the letter and the maharaja's enthusiasm. He had already received favourable reports from

Reverend W.J. Jay, the chaplain at Fatehgarh and Archdeacon Pratt.

Lord Dalhousie replied to Duleep Singh on 15 February 1853:

My dear Maharaja,

I have received with the most lively satisfaction the letter in which you express your desire to be at once baptized, and to be admitted as a member of the Church of Christ. When you first showed an inclination to believe in the truths, which you found, declared in the word of God, I advised you not to act hastily, to continue in your study of the Bible, and to test by time the strength and sincerity of your belief.

You have followed my advice, and I have learnt with real pleasure from the statement of the Archdeacon and Rev. Jay that they have found you quite fit to receive the baptism you desire to obtain. I, on my part, most readily assent to your wish, and I thank the God and Saviour of us all, who had put into your heart a knowledge of, and a belief in, the truth of our holy religion, and that you may show to your countrymen in India an example of a pure and blameless life such as befits a Christian prince.

I beg your highness to believe in the strength and sincerity of the regard in which I shall ever feel towards you, and to remain, now and always,

Your Highness's sincere and affectionate friend.

Dalhousie

Soon after receiving Lord Dalhousie's letter, Duleep Singh started preparing himself for baptism in great earnest. He began to discard any object which reminded him of his religion of birth. Duleep Singh had many idols made of precious materials in his residence. His servants readily accepted figurines of gold, silver, jade, ivory and sandalwood, which the maharaja no longer wanted to keep in his mansion. One day, he brought a beautifully crafted brass idol of Lord Krishna to Lena Login. It was one of the idols left behind, since it did not have much value. Duleep Singh handed her the nearly two-feet high icon and said, 'I don't need this idol anymore. I don't want to be reminded that I did pooja to it.' Lena Login kept the statuette with her for its exquisiteness; it later became a highly coveted family heirloom.

The baptism ceremony of Maharaja Duleep Singh was fixed for 8 March 1853. As desired by Lord Dalhousie, it was to be a private affair and Maharaja Duleep Singh was to retain his name.

Reverend William Jay was requested to administer the rite. Since the local church was under repair, the ceremony was held in the mansion of Maharaja Duleep Singh. All the British officers and their families stationed in Fatehgarh were present for the momentous occasion. Duleep Singh's friends, relatives and servants were all there to witness the unique ritual, which was the first to be undertaken by a member of an Indian royal family on Indian soil. They were all aware of Princess Gowramma of Coorg, who had made a similar 'profession of her faith in the Redeemer's blood' in the presence of Queen Victoria at London, about a year ago. The American Presbyterian priest, Reverend J. Johnston Walsh, and a few of his colleagues from the nearby Fatehgarh Mission, were also present to witness the holy baptism.

Dressed in his traditional robes, Duleep Singh maintained a dignified and earnest demeanour during the ritual. He answered the questions Reverend Jay put to him as part of the ceremony, in a firm, reverent and decisive tone. During the ceremony, Reverend Jay suddenly realised that there was no water from river Jordan, which was required for the baptism. Lena Login spontaneously suggested, 'Why don't we use water from the holy Ganges?' There was enthusiastic acceptance of this idea, and Reverend Jay agreed to make an exception. One of the maharaja's servants dashed towards the holy river and fetched a vessel full of the sacred water. After Duleep Singh received the sacrament, Dr Login, Lena Login, Walter Guise and Colonel Alexander signed the register as witnesses. Maharaja Duleep Singh was thus formally admitted into the Presbyterian Christian Church.

There was great appreciation of Maharaja Duleep Singh's conversion by the Christian community. The American priest, Reverend Walsh, best expressed the feelings of the Westerners, in these lofty words:

> The result of these efforts has been such as, in our minds, to outweigh in value the Koh-i-noor diamond, which he contributed to England's justly beloved and happy Queen. He lost his earthly jewels, but gained by it a heavenly one. He exchanged a worldly crown for a better and more enduring one above; and the loss of his kingdom here has ensured, we trust, admission to the kingdom of heaven. It shows, too, how wisely God orders his providence, that what at first appears a very sad and afflictive dispensation, results in untold advantages. It so, doubtless, appeared to the Maharaja, and he probably felt the loss of his kingdom, and the honours attached to it; but he now feels that had he remained and reigned in his native land, he would have been left to evil influences, and not improbably would have died, like his uncles and predecessors, a violent death.

Princess Victoria Gowramma.
Etching of a painting by
Franz Xaver Winterhalter, 1854.

Painting of Maharaja Duleep
Singh by Franz Xaver
Winterhalter, 1854.

Maharaja Duleep Singh. Marble bust by
Baron Carlo Marochetti, 1856.
(Courtesy The Royal Collection © 2009,
Her Majesty Queen Elizabeth II)

Veerarajendra with Princess Victoria Gowramma in London,
with his attendants

Princess Victoria Gowramma,
November 1854.
Photograph by Roger Fenton.
(Courtesy The Royal collection ©
2009, Her Majesty Queen
Elizabeth II)

FEMME DU RADJA DE KOURG.

Sketch of Mudduveeramma,
wife of Veerarajendra, while
in London

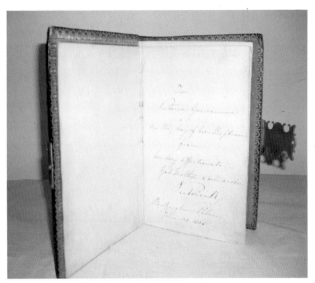

Queen Victoria's autograph on the Bible she presented to
Princess Victoria Gowramma in 1852.

Marble bust of Princess Victoria Gowramma by Baron Carlo
Marochetti, 1856. Painted and gilded by William H. Millais
(Courtesy The Royal Collection © 2009, Her Majesty Queen Elizabeth I

Sir John Spencer Login

Lady Lena Campbell Login

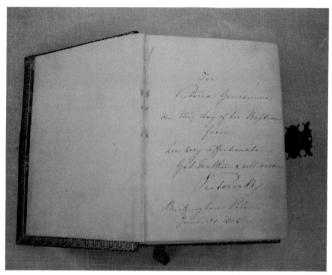

Autographed Bible presented by Queen Victoria to Princess Victoria
Gowramma on the day of her baptism in 1852

Bible presented by Queen Victoria to
Princess Victoria Gowramma, 1852

Maharaja Duleep Singh, photographed by his teacher
Dr Ernest Becker, August 1854, at Osborne House.

Prince Albert with Queen Victoria, 1860

Queen Victoria by Franz Xaver Winterhalter, 1859

Dalhousie wrote on 12 March 1853, to his friend, Sir George Couper, expressing similar sentiments:

On 8 March 1853 a very remarkable event in history and in every way gratifying was enacted at Fatehgarh – the baptism of Maharaja Duleep Singh. I am convinced that, if ever the shadow of the hand of God was made visible to mortal sight, in a human transaction of these later days, it has been visible here in the turning of this boy's heart from darkness to light. This is the first Indian prince of many who have succumbed to our power or have acknowledged it that has adopted the faith of the stranger. Who shall say to what it may lead? God prosper and multiply it! I have never from the hour in which I signed the decree had one moment's hesitation or doubt to the justice or necessity of my act in dethroning the boy. If I had such a doubt, the sight of the blessed result for him to which that act led would now have thoroughly consoled me for what I did then. As it is, my mind is doubly content as to what he lost; immeasurably content as to the gain he has found in his loss. I hope that before long the court will allow him to go to England. He is wild to be allowed to do so, not that he wishes to be made a fool of, like the Rajah of Coorg, or Jung Bahadur, but because his fancy is to be European in all his tastes, and he is dying to see Europe and all its wonders. He told me he used to dream every night that he was visiting the Duke of Wellington. That dream, unhappily, can never come true.

Lord Dalhousie felt better after penning this letter to his friend London. He had been criticised at home by a section of the erals for his unprincipled actions in annexing Punjab. He could ly justify his actions by taking the moral high ground.

Dr John Login was eager to take the newly converted Christian maharaja to England as soon as possible. Duleep Singh's curiosity about London and other places in England grew by the day as he read more and more English magazines and newspapers. The *Illustrated London News* was his favourite. He enthusiastically read the news and visualised the various places illustrated. He frequently asked his English friends to tell him all about England. Dr Login made Duleep Singh write another letter to Lord Dalhousie to request the governor-general to give him permission to visit England.

Duleep Singh wrote: 'I wish to say that I am very anxious to go, and quite ready to start whenever his Lordship gives me permission. I do not want to go to make a show of myself, but to study and complete my education, and I wish to live in England as quietly as possible.'

Dr Login forwarded this letter of Duleep Singh to the governor general with a covering letter. Lord Dalhousie's reply came, soon after, addressed to Dr Login:

We are one in thinking he should go to England. It is my opinion, as it is yours, that he should go while he is yet what we should consider a boy. I shall therefore ask permission from the Court to let him go next spring, if you consider him ready and desirous, as before, to go. I will not disguise from you that the Court may not give a very gracious assent; the visit of Jung Bahadur, spoiled and still more, the present visit of the ex-Raja of Coorg, whom, in spite of all my precautions and warning they have lifted wholly out of his place, making a fool both of him and of themselves thereby, has disgusted the Court and the Board of Control with native, and especially with princely visitors. Still I hope they will agree, and still more, I hope that the Maharaja will not expect pompous receptions, and will rather seek quiet privacy while he shall remain in England.

Dalhousie had further stated, 'I am an advocate of maharaja Duleep Singh going to England if it should help a marriage between him and the little princess of Coorg. I shall be very glad for it will reconcile much which would otherwise be a considerable perplexity both in her case and his.'

In January 1854, Dalhousie received communication from the Court of Directors of the East India Company in London, giving their consent for Maharaja Duleep Singh to visit England. There was great celebration when this news reached Fatehgarh Park. Duleep Singh was very excited at the thought of crossing the oceans in magnificent ships, travelling to new lands and visiting all the wonderful places in England that he had got acquainted with through reading and listening to his friends. Duleep Singh was very keen that his nephew Sahdev Singh too should accompany him to England. Sahdev Singh was equally interested and the British gave their permission, happy to see another claimant to the throne of Lahore out of the way. However, the young boy's mother, Rani Duknu, protested vehemently and prevented him from following Duleep Singh. Ever since the conversion of Duleep Singh, Rani Duknu had distanced herself from Duleep Singh. She reluctantly showed respect to the maharaja who had committed the unpardonable act of breaking his religion. As required by protocol she kissed his hand, but had a bath soon after!

Preparation for the long-awaited voyage started in right earnest. Dr Login and Lena Login advised Duleep Singh on the type of clothing suitable for the journey and later at London. New clothes were stitched for the winter months. Duleep Singh packed his formal robes for the occasions when he would be meeting the

English royalty, including, he hoped, the queen. Duleep Singh wanted his Hindu friend, Bhajan Lal, to accompany him to England. Though interested, Bhajan Lal was not permitted by his family who had plans to establish a tent-manufacturing unit, a lucrative business in those days. Besides, his orthodox parents did not want their son to cross the seas.

The maharaja's English valet Thornton readily agreed to continue his assignment in England. Duleep Singh had to take leave of his English friend Tommy Scott, who went back to stay with his widowed mother. Walter Guise was paid a bonus of 5,000 rupees for his efforts in tutoring the maharaja. Duleep Singh's servants who were to stay behind were highly emotional. Financial arrangements were made for the upkeep of his establishment at Fatehgarh Park. He assured them, 'I will return to Fatehgarh soon after completing my studies in England. Please take care of my elephants and horses.' He had, however, decided to take his favourite falcons to England. Dr Login's assistant, Sergeant Elliot, was appointed the caretaker of the maharaja's house and other assets at Fatehgarh.

Finally in early April 1854, the maharaja and his party left Fatehgarh for Calcutta to board the ship to London. Lord Dalhousie made it clear to Dr Login regarding the protocol for the deposed maharaja—mounted escort, and twenty-one-gun salute while on Indian soil. 'However,' Dalhousie emphasised, 'His Highness should know that while he receives all the honours of his rank here, in England he would be entitled only to courtesy.'

The entourage halted at Lucknow and spent some time with the Resident Colonel William Sleeman. The Logins had an opportunity to meet old acquaintances from their earlier stint there. They had many friends amongst the British and the royal family of Oudh. Colonel Sleeman was most taken with the handsome young maharaja. He was a keen ethnologist and tried to impress upon Duleep Singh his views that the Jats of Punjab and the Jutes from Kent had the same ancestry.

Their next stop was Benares, where they met a brahmin named Pundit Nehemiah Goreh. He was one of the first high-caste Hindus in Benares to embrace Christianity. He had taken 'Nehemiah' as his Christian name, and was actively involved in teaching the Gospel to his fellow Indians. Having heard of Duleep Singh's conversion to Christianity, Pundit Goreh came to meet the maharaja and the Logins during their stopover in Benares. He enthusiastically shared his spiritual experiences with them. Pundit Goreh had received the news of Princess Gowramma's baptism in London in the presence of Queen Victoria. He was also well acquainted with Veerarajendra, and had visited the raja many times in Coorg Nest. As a member of the Church of England, he was a candidate to receive the holy order. It was Pundit Nehemiah Goreh's burning ambition to visit London to broaden his understanding of Christian theology.

Pundit Goreh had many meetings with the Logins and Duleep Singh during their short sojourn in Benares. He requested Duleep Singh: 'Maharaja, please let me accompany you to London as your Christian guru. I can also tutor you in Oriental languages. All I want in return is food, clothing and simple accommodation.' The brahmin reminded Duleep Singh, 'Your father, the great Lion of Punjab, donated gold to cover the two domes of the famous Kashi Viswanath temple here. He is held in great esteem by the people of this holy city.'

The highly knowledgeable Indian impressed the Logins, and they were convinced that he would be an ideal companion for the maharaja. Dr Login used his influence with Lord Dalhousie to obtain permission for the Pundit to join the maharaja's entourage. The Logins were pleased that they had found a far superior replacement to Bhajan Lal, who had declined to accompany the maharaja to London. In accordance with his wishes, Pundit Nehemiah was given permission to travel to England and remain there for three years along with the maharaja.

Lord Dalhousie, who was tracking the progress of the maharaja's movement, was keen on meeting his ward before he set out on his voyage. By the time the convoy of Duleep Singh reached the outskirts of Calcutta, Lord Dalhousie had many guests staying at the Government House. He sent instructions to accommodate the maharaja and his party at his weekend residence at Barrackpore. Duleep Singh and his associates were provided Dalhousie's personal boat 'Soona Mookee' to make the trip up the Hoogly River to reach Barrackpore.

Prior to their departure, the governor-general invited the maharaja and the Logins to dine at his official residence. Lord Dalhousie was pleased to find the young maharaja speaking good English, and much improved in his knowledge of various subjects since their last meeting at Fatehgarh. He engaged Duleep Singh in lengthy conversations and advised Duleep Singh as to how he should conduct himself during his stay at London. 'Your Highness's primary purpose of sailing to Britain is to enhance your knowledge and to acquaint yourself with the progress in Europe. Concentrate on your education and in broadening your understanding of the glorious religion you have chosen to embrace.'

When the maharaja's party boarded their ship on 19 April 1854, a farewell letter from the governor-general, along with a beautifully-bound Bible as a gift, was delivered to Duleep Singh. In it, Dalhousie had inscribed:

This Holy Book in which your Highness has been led by God's grace to find an inheritance richer by far than all earthly kingdom.

In a covering letter, Dalhousie wrote:

My dear Maharaja,

Before you quit India, I have been desirous of offering you a parting gift, which in future years might sometimes remind you of me.

Since that day when the course of public events placed you a little boy in my hands, I have regarded you in some sort as my son. I therefore ask you, before we part, to accept from me the volume, which I should offer to my own child, as the best of all gifts, since in it alone is to be found the secret of real happiness either in this world or that which is to come.

I bid you farewell, my dear Maharaja, and beg you to believe me always, with sincere regards, your Highness's faithful friend,

Dalhousie

The governor-general later wrote to his friend George Couper about the maharaja and his meeting with him:

Maharaja Duleep Singh, though at an awkward age his manners are apparently nice and gentlemanly.

If you should see anything of the Maharaja, and of Dr Login, I hope you will discourage any idea you may detect of taking the lad to public meetings, especially Exeter Hall ones there to be paraded as a Christianized prince. I have warned him against it, but I am a little afraid of the temptation when it comes close; and I wish to guard against it, for it would be very bad

for the boy. I presented Nisbet's Bible to him as a parting gift.
It is a splendid work, apart from its written contents.

Lord Dalhousie was, however, sure that Maharaja Duleep
Singh, now a confirmed Christian, would not return to India once
he got accustomed to life in England. Duleep Singh had blatantly
broken his caste and upset the Sikh Khalsa, and there was no
threat of the citizens of Punjab ever rallying behind him even
in the event of his return. He hoped that the much-speculated
alliance between Duleep Singh and Princess Victoria Gowramma
of Coorg could take place sooner than later. He too envisioned
great possibilities for Christianity in India from the union of these
two Indian royalties. Their union would be a shining example
for other Indian royalties.

The fifteen-year-old Duleep Singh could hardly contain his
excitement on setting sail to England. His dream had come true.
There was an impressive twenty-one-gun salute in his honour
as he boarded the ship at Calcutta port. It was a clear day and
the sea was calm. He and his Indian servants watched in awe as
the ship began to sail away from the shores. There were brief
stopovers at Madras and Colombo. On Lord Dalhousie's orders,
the maharaja received official salute from the military at every
port in Indian waters where they dropped anchor. Their ship soon
entered the Arabian Sea and headed towards Egypt. Lena Login
captured Duleep Singh's attention with the captivating story of
the legendary priest-king, Prester John, who supposedly ruled an
idyllic Christian kingdom deep in the African continent.

As in the case of Veerarajendra and Princess Gowramma, their
schedule was to disembark at Port Suez at the head of the Gulf
of Suez in Egypt. Thereon they would travel to Cairo by road.
They would spend a week at Cairo as guests of the Khedive or

the Viceroy—Ibrahim Said Pasha. From Cairo, they would proceed towards the harbour at Alexandria on the northern tip of Egypt, to board another ship to take them to London. The Logins had planned daily classes to familiarise the maharaja with geographical details of the route they were sailing through. Pundit Nehemiah Goreh also started his classes, but Duleep Singh did not find them quite as engrossing as the various ports they were visiting.

Before they reached Egypt, the Logins gave him a detailed historical background of the pharaohs, the pyramids, and the unique hieroglyphics. Nearly a month after leaving Calcutta, the ship skirted the Horn of Africa and entered the Red Sea after a couple of days stopover at Aden. Dr Login explained to Duleep Singh about an ambitious project undertaken by the French to construct a canal to connect the Red Sea to the Mediterranean Sea. This canal would allow ships to avoid the circuitous route round the Cape. It would also eliminate the need to travel by road to Alexandria.

Lord Dalhousie had written in advance to the British Resident at Cairo, Mr Bruce, to extend all possible assistance to Maharaja Duleep Singh and their entourage. The Khedive Ibrahim Said Pasha went out of his way to place one of his well-appointed four-horse carriages at the disposal of the maharaja to visit important sights in Cairo. It was a fun-filled week as they explored the fascinating monuments in the ancient city. Duleep Singh delighted himself in vicarious pleasure as he raced his companions to the top of the pyramid. The Arab guides provided by Mr Bruce were quite fed up with the maharaja's juvenile behaviour, but tolerated his antics in anticipation of handsome *baksheesh*! On the other hand, the Logins and the servants of the maharaja were concerned that the valuable strands of pearls that he always wore might snap as in an earlier occasion, scattering the beads all over the desert sand. Duleep Singh frequently broke into peels of uncontrollable laughter at the anxiety of his companions.

In Cairo, the Logins arranged a visit to the American Missionary School for Duleep Singh to see how young girls were educated in true Christian values. Duleep Singh was deeply impressed with what he saw in this institution (years later, he was to come here in search of a suitable bride). After their memorable stay at Cairo, the party moved north and finally reached the port city of Alexandria to embark on their onward journey.

After two days' halt at the historic city of Alexandria, they boarded the vessel SS Hindustan that would take them to the shores of England. The weather in the Mediterranean was turbulent, which made the sailing quite rough. A week later, they anchored at the port in the island of Malta. At this British stronghold, they were surprised to be welcomed with a twenty-one-gun salute to the maharaja. They took a leisurely tour of the island while the ship was serviced and loaded with necessities. A brief stop over at Cagliari and another week's sailing brought them to the strategic British colony of Gibraltar. Here again, the entourage was pleasantly surprised to receive a twenty-one-gun salute in honour of the Indian maharaja. Duleep Singh was elated at the importance given to him.

Dr Login then revealed to him, 'Lord Dalhousie gave his orders for these show of respect to your rank during this voyage. However, the governor-general has asked me to tell you that once in Britain you would not be entitled to these protocols, and will only be shown courtesy normally extended to British nobility.' The excitement of soon reaching his dream city overcame Duleep Singh's concerns of how he would be received by British society

As their ship sailed through the Strait of Gibraltar, there was an impressive silence as the passengers sighted the majestic Rock of Gibraltar. As a matter of interest, Duleep Singh and Pundit Goreh were given special permission to be with the captain of the ship to observe for themselves the exact moment their ship entered the Atlantic Ocean.

The ship, caught in a gale, rolled and tossed as they sailed into the Atlantic. After nearly two weeks on the high seas, the ship entered the English Channel. A few days later, they came within sight of Plymouth, where they anchored for a couple of days. Duleep Singh bode farewell to many of the passengers who disembarked at Plymouth, a major port. Their sea voyage finally ended at the port of Southampton.

It was mid-summer when they reached their destination. Duleep Singh and his party travelled by train from Southampton to London. He was delighted to identify many of the buildings and landmarks as they neared London. He repeatedly exclaimed, 'In London at last!' His first impression of the teeming metropolis was marred by the overpowering smell of the Thames. Duleep Singh's valet Thornton cautioned him of a belief at the time that constant breathing of the miasma, the foul air, caused cholera.

The Logins took Duleep Singh to the fashionable Mivart's Hotel (later renamed Claridge's), on Brooke Street where the Court of Directors of the East India Company had booked rooms for the Indian maharaja and his companions. Two years earlier, Veerarajendra and his daughter, Princess Gowramma, had been accommodated in the same hotel. The proprietress, Marianna Claridge, on instructions from the Company, did not accord any special reception to the maharaja.

Duleep Singh was excited to finally be in London, the city of his dreams and the culmination of his childhood hopes. He was now impatient to set out on an excursion of the famed city. A coach tour of London was arranged two days after they settled down in their hotel rooms. As they visited the various landmarks, the young maharaja in his dashing robe attracted a lot of attention from the curious bystanders. His attire was a combination of Indian and Western clothes. He wore his colourful headdress and the trademark strands of pearls. There were already write-ups in the newspapers about the sixteen-year-old Indian maharaja who had voluntarily embraced Christianity. One elderly woman came up to Duleep Singh and said, 'Your Highness, I congratulate you on accepting the truth in the holy Bible. Hope your subjects too will follow suit.' Another lady wanted to know, 'Will you be marrying the goddaughter of the queen, the young Christian Princess Victoria Gowramma?' Duleep Singh responded with his childish laughter.

During the last week of June, an eagerly-awaited letter was delivered to the maharaja from the queen's secretary. It was an invitation for Duleep Singh to meet Queen Victoria and Prince Albert at Buckingham Palace in the afternoon of 1 July 1854.

Duleep Singh could hardly contain his excitement. Even though there was a week for the occasion, he started preparing for the event. The Logins advised him to dress formally as he did for his darbars. He had outgrown his formal clothes since he last wore them in Fatehgarh before his baptism. Tailors were called in to stitch and adjust the robes to suit his new height and size. His waist had become slimmer. A barber came to trim his beard and moustache. His jewellery and strands of pearls were given a fine polish. The Logins did not want another occurrence of the pearls coming unstrung, especially in the presence of the queen and all the other important people at the palace. There were several rounds of rehearsals as to how Duleep Singh would curtsy to the queen and the proper way to address the royalty. 'Don't laugh loudly, and do not interrupt the queen when she is talking to you,' Lena Login advised the maharaja, fearful of his tendency to go into paroxysms of laughter.

A few days earlier, a formal communication had come from Buckingham Palace, informing that Duleep Singh would be addressed as 'His Highness, the maharaja'. The Logins were pleased that their ward had been granted a high order of rank.

An elegant four-horse carriage was hired to take His Highness Maharaja Duleep Singh to Buckingham Palace. His coachman, Thornton, was close at hand for any assistance. On the appointed day, he woke up earlier than usual. He took great care with each item of his attire. He wore necklaces, pendants, broaches, bracelets, and five strands of pearl chokers with matching pearl earrings. He had a ring on every finger. The *piece de resistance* was the gem-studded pendant with the image of Queen Victoria. He sparkled with all the diamonds and precious stones embellishing his robes, turban and footware. Dr Login, however, firmly dissuaded him from carrying his ceremonial sword.

After a light lunch, the party was ready to leave for Buckingham Palace. Lena Login complimented him, 'Your Highness, Maharaja Duleep Singh, you look handsome and graceful.' With a mock flourish, Duleep Singh squared his shoulders and stepped out with his head held high. Thornton respectfully held the door open for him as he entered the waiting coach.

Duleep Singh was received at the entrance to Buckingham Palace by the palace staff and was ushered into the impressive room where the queen usually met her private visitors. He was formally presented to the queen and her royal consort, Prince Albert. Duleep Singh was most graceful in his demeanour. He looked dashing in his impressive costume. Queen Victoria and Prince Albert took an instant liking to the youthful and handsome maharaja. They had studied in detail the background of the young maharaja, and the history of the Punjab. During the course of their meeting, one of the first reactions of the queen was to announce that her favourite artist, Franz Xaver Winterhalter, would paint a full-length portrait of His Highness, Maharaja Duleep Singh. She wanted the maharaja to wear the same resplendent royal regalia for the portrait.

The queen-mother joined the royal couple to meet the special guest in the palace. The royal family was impressed with the near-perfect English spoken by the young maharaja from India. They all admired the fine young man, and appreciated his sophisticated manners. In private, they discussed what an excellent pair the young maharaja and the thirteen-year-old princess Victoria Gowramma would make. It seemed like a match divinely predestined.

Queen Victoria, who maintained an impeccable diary, wrote a detailed account of the day, adding the following comment:

> The Koh-i-noor diamond once belonged to, and was worn by the Maharaja. I always feel so much for these poor deposed Indian Princes.

The queen was not entirely comfortable with the manner in which the famed stone had come to her possession. The large, rather clumsily-cut diamond had been since reshaped and reduced to nearly half its size in Amsterdam, and given completely different facets. She expressed her deep anxiety to Prince Albert. They both resolved to make amends to the maharaja, whom they found to be a straightforward and upright young man.

Within a week of this first meeting, Duleep Singh was invited to a grand dinner party at Buckingham Palace. The queen had also invited several of her close associates and members of the family. She was keen on getting the maharaja acquainted with her children. His Highness Maharaja Duleep Singh was seated next to the queen—an honour given only to high-ranking royalty. The Logins tutored maharaja to talk to the queen about his happiness after embracing Christianity. Duleep Singh genuinely felt a sense of contentment having broken his caste; he was full of pride in following a superior religion. Dr Login reminded Duleep Singh to observe all the etiquettes and said to the young maharaja: 'Please desist from talking with food in your mouth. Take small morsels at a time.'

Maharaja Duleep Singh's conduct at the formal dinner was exceptionally refined. The royal family was suitably impressed. He made interesting conversation, and his observations on religion were highly appreciated by the queen and her consort. The queen had already commissioned her favourite artist Winterhalter to start on the maharaja's portrait the very next week. Duleep Singh would have to go to Buckingham Place for several sittings where the artist would work on the project.

After the guests departed, the queen mentioned to Prince Albert, 'We need to have a companion painting of Princess Victoria Gowramma executed by Winterhalter.' Princess Gowramma had by then spent a year with the Drummonds at Scotland, but the teenaged princess was not happy living in the dull countryside. She yearned to be in London. She was depressed and her relationship with the Drummonds was not as cordial as earlier. She did not enjoy the strict routine imposed by her guardians, and was especially miserable during the long winter months.

To make matters worse, one day she found herself haemorrhaging and was terrified that her end had come. The only two people she wished she had nearby were Subadhramma and Gangamma. Mrs Drummond found her crying in her room and after much coaxing, Gowramma confided in her. Gowramma was confused when Mrs Drummond laughed and told her, 'Princess, you are now a woman. You should be rejoicing.' Failing to find anything to cheer about, Gowramma was confused and further dejected. The Drummonds communicated to the queen the coming of age of her goddaughter. In spite of their preoccupations with matters concerning the state, the queen and Prince Albert were eager to bring about the marriage alliance between Princess Gowramma and Maharaja Duleep Singh. The queen instructed her Secretary, Sir Charles Phipps, to initiate steps to achieve this union between the two Indian royals.

Winterhalter started painting Maharaja Duleep Singh's portrait at the White Drawing Room in Buckingham Palace. Duleep Singh had to come attired in his royal regalia adorned with all the ornaments. The maharaja wore his blue and gold dress with the matching turban. Prominent was the pendant with the queen's visage. He had to strike a pose wherein he leaned slightly on a ceremonial sword held in his right hand. Each day, the session lasted for about two hours, and the maharaja was most cooperative. Pundit Goreh frequently accompanied Duleep Singh. Winterhalter was pleased with his subject. The famed artist was most impressed at the handsome features and nobility of the young Indian royalty who stood still for the sketching for hours without complaining. For Winterhalter, who had painted portraits of several European royals, Duleep Singh was one of his favourite personalities whose unique oriental charm he was able to capture on canvas. The queen and Prince Albert dropped by the White Drawing Room frequently to watch the progress of the work of art. Queen Victoria, herself a good artist, drew sketches of Duleep Singh's profile and that of his companion Pundit Nehemiah Goreh for her diary.

One day, while Duleep Singh was posing for his portrait, Queen Victoria came quietly and sat next to Lena Login. The queen asked her in a hushed voice, 'Has the maharaja ever talked to you about the Koh-i-noor? Does he regret having lost possession of it?'

Lena Login replied that while in India the maharaja did speak about the famed rock. 'He wore the bracelet, in which the diamond was encrusted, during ceremonial occasions, particularly on his birthday.'

Queen Victoria wanted Lena Login to find out discreetly if Duleep Singh wished to see the diamond, though it had been now cut and reshaped.

Lena Login casually brought up the issue of the Koh-i-noor diamond while they were riding back in the carriage. The maharaja enthusiastically responded that he would love to see the 'mountain of light', one of his most valuable inheritances. 'I last wore it on my tenth birthday celebration at Lahore,' he recalled.

During the maharaja's next session at Buckingham Palace, the queen and Prince Albert sat silently watching Winterhalter paint his subject. A while later, Lena Login was startled when a group of sturdy beefeaters in their unique uniform, entered the room escorting an official bearing a small casket, which was handed over to Her Majesty. The queen opened the box and took out the

Koh-i-noor diamond, now half its original size, and walked over to the maharaja, saying 'Maharaja, I have something to show you!'

Duleep Singh stepped down from the dais where he was posing for the portrait, and reverentially held the diamond. He stood still and stared at Her Majesty for a while, and then looked at the famed gem cradled in his hands. He did seem disappointed at the reduced size of the diamond. He viewed the newly cut stone from various angles, and took it to the window for better inspection. The maharaja was engrossed in examining the diamond. He did not say a word. There was an uneasy silence in the room.

The queen, Prince Albert and Lena Login felt anxious as to what the young man's intentions were. At one point, it seemed as though the former owner of the Koh-i-noor might demand return of the diamond, or in anger fling the diamond out of the window! However, after what appeared to be an eon, Duleep Singh sighed and walked towards the queen. He reverentially placed the diamond in the queen's hands and said: 'It is to me, Ma'am, the greatest of pleasure thus to have the opportunity, as a loyal subject, of myself tendering to my sovereign the Koh-i-noor.' This most unexpected and magnanimous response from the young maharaja stunned everyone in the room. The queen was relieved and her feeling of guilt lifted a little. After this incident, her affection for Duleep Singh doubled, and she was determined to help the charming maharaja, and do all that could be done to befriend and protect him.

When this news of Duleep Singh declaring the Koh-i-noor diamond as a gift from him to the queen reached Lord Dalhousie, the governor-general was not amused. Privately he wrote to Sir George Couper strongly asserting that it was part of war reparation. Besides the 'mountain of light', many precious stones and jewellery were also confiscated to recover the cost of fighting two wars in the Punjab, which were, according to Dalhousie, fought to protect the young Maharaja Duleep Singh! Lord Dalhousie asserted that he, on behalf of the East India Company, had presented most of these personal treasures of the maharaja to the queen.

For Duleep Singh, events were taking place at a rapid pace ever since his arrival in London. The importance given to the deposed Indian maharaja by Her Majesty was a hotly debated issue in government circles. During the end of August, Queen Victoria invited the maharaja to spend time at her Italianate palazzo in Osborne on the Isle of Wight. The queen and Prince Albert wished Duleep Singh to be well acquainted with their children. Duleep Singh soon became popular with all the royal offsprings. He was particularly protective of the haemophilic Prince Leopold, the youngest of the eight children of the queen at the time.

To put to rest all the unwarranted debates, the queen, in an unprecedented move, announced that Maharaja Duleep Singh would take the rank of 'prince', equal to those of European princes bearing the title of His Serene Highness. In court protocol, he took precedence next to the Royal family. The directors of the East India Company were shocked, and commented the queen was 'spoiling' the dethroned oriental ruler. Queen Victoria brushed aside these comments and stuck to her decision. Similarly, Princess Gowramma too was accorded the status equivalent to European princesses.

At Osborne, the queen and her consort had the opportunity to talk to Duleep Singh at length. Duleep Singh opened his heart to the royal couple, and confided in them why he had rejected his own religion and embraced Christianity. They were very happy when he went on to pronounce, 'Missionaries should go to India, particularly Punjab—for now is the time to convince those Indians who have not converted from conviction, that by becoming Christians they have obtained every earthly advantage and eternal happiness hereafter.'

Sir George Couper gave Lord Dalhousie a detailed account of Duleep Singh's stay at Osborne. In reply, Dalhousie expressed his earlier apprehensions of the queen spoiling the young and impressionable maharaja. The governor-general feared that deposed rulers would expect special treatment from the government of India. Being a stickler for protocol, Lord Dalhousie was clear in his mind that the deposed royalty came below the governor-general in the order of precedence. He wrote to Sir Couper: 'The maharaja should have no doubts in his mind the necessity of leaving his shoes at the door of the governor-general's room, when he is admitted to visit him.'

Dalhousie's tirades against the Indian royalties were, however confined to his close friends. Queen Victoria, on the other hand, extended to Duleep Singh and Veerarajendra the protocol befitting royalty. On 12 August 1854, Maharaja Duleep Singh and Veerarajendra were prominent invitees at the Prorogation of the Parliament by Her Majesty, the queen. By the command of the queen, they were seated close to the Throne. *The Times, London* of 14 August 1854 reported:

...Maharaja Duleep Singh and the Raja of Coorg were clad in the most exquisite products of the looms of India. Their shawls and silks of gold and silver tissue, covered with 'barbaric pearls and gold,' attracted many admiring glances, and the eyes of the Royalty itself paused to rest upon the easy and graceful folds of their attire, by the side of which the garments of the civilized Europe looked infinitely prosaic and devoid of taste.

The queen's secretary, Sir Charles Phipps, in a letter dated 5 September 1854 to Dr Login, alluded to the serious intentions of Her Majesty in bringing about an alliance between Maharaja Duleep Singh and Princess Victoria Gowramma.

> The more I think upon the subject, the more it appears to me that these two young people are pointed out for each other. The only two Christians of high rank of their own countries, both having the advantage of early European influences, there seems to be many points of sympathy between them. They are both religious, both fond of music, both gentle in their natures. I know that the Queen thinks that this would be the best arrangement for both their happiness, provided that they were to like each other of course, without this no happiness could exist. Of course the Queen takes a great interest in the little Princess, as Her Majesty considers Herself as more than a godmother to her.

Queen Victoria was highly appreciative of the manner in which the Login couple had managed the affairs of His Highness, Maharaja Duleep Singh. For a boy of sixteen, the Indian maharaja was well versed in the contents of the Bible. His knowledge of English was admirable. In addition, he was familiar with all the customs and manners of the West. The queen conferred the coveted knighthood on Dr John Login in November 1854, in recognition of his services.

On 21 November 1854, the queen invited Princess Victoria Gowramma to Windsor Castle so that the latter could become better acquainted with the royal children. It was also the occasion of the fourteenth birthday party of Princess Royal (Princess Victoria, the eldest daughter of the queen). Princess Gowramma now spoke English fluently, having spent more than two years in England. She and the eleven-year-old Princess Alice became good friends. The queen and Prince Albert were pleased to see that Gowramma's upbringing by the Drummonds had vastly improved her personality and self-confidence. They agreed with each other that the young Christian princess from Coorg was well groomed to be Maharaja Duleep Singh's consort.

Gowramma and Duleep Singh had heard a great deal about each other from their guardians. They were well aware of the matchmaking that was going on. While at Fatehgarh, Duleep Singh himself had seriously considered marrying Princess Gowramma, even though he had not met her. The teenage princess too often daydreamed about receiving a marriage proposal from the maharaja.

Informal get-togethers were arranged by their respective guardians, so that Maharaja Duleep Singh and Princess Victoria Gowramma could meet and interact with each other. It was fervently hoped that familiarity would soon blossom into love. For the princess and the maharaja, their first few meetings were rather awkward. Subsequently they met on several occasions and became well acquainted with each other. They exchanged notes about their studies and the places they had visited in England. Duleep Singh was interested in knowing more about Scotland from Gowramma. He had made a brief trip to Edinburgh and had stayed with Lord Dalhousie's daughters. The Logins noticed that the young princess was impressed by the maharaja, though the latter did not display any noticeable reaction and remained formal.

Along with Gowramma, Veerarajendra too visited the maharaja at Kew on a few occasions. The raja had heard about the Logins from Dr Jeaffreson and from his son-in-law, Jung Bahadur of Nepal. He lost no time in making friends with Sir John Login and Lady Lena Login. After this meeting, Veerarajendra frequently sought their assistance in his legal battle against the East India Company. With Sir Login's help, the raja kept in touch with his family in Benares, and ensured they received part of his pension.

The queen was quite happy that her plans for the maharaja and the princess were progressing on the anticipated lines. In her letter dated 24 November 1854 to Lord Dalhousie, she mentioned her two Indian protégés:

> The young people have met and were pleased with each other, so that the Queen hopes that their union will in the course of time come to pass. Her little goddaughter has been here lately and though still childish for her age (she is nearly fourteen) is pretty, lively, intelligent and going on satisfactorily in her education. Of the Maharaja...we can only speak in terms of praise. He promises to be a bright example to all Indian Princes—for he is thoroughly good and amiable and most anxious to improve himself.

Sir Login too was pleased with the outcome of these meetings between the two Indian royals. He wrote to Lord Dalhousie with details of the encounters:

> ...I have already acquainted your Lordship that Maharajah Duleep has had an opportunity of meeting the Coorg Princess, and that he was favourably impressed with what he had seen of her. She is, indeed, an amicable and engaging little girl, and so far as one can judge, is likely to turn out well. Mrs Drummond

has brought her several times to visit my wife and children, and the Maharajah has also twice called on the Princess and Mrs Drummond, with me. I am, however, very anxious, that any advances towards intimacy should come from himself, and I know that although he is inclined to be pleased with her, he is rather apprehensive of leading her to expect too much from his attentions. I have little doubt, if it were not for her father's character, and the dread he has of coming into contact with him, he would be more disposed to cultivate acquaintance with her. As I have, however, been lately engaged in reading *History of the Sikhs* with him, and especially Carmichael Smyth's *Reigning Family of Lahore*, he perceives that, in respect to their parents, they are similarly situated, and that the same feeling which may prevent him from wishing to be connected with the Rajah of Coorg's family, is likely to be an obstacle to his forming an alliance elsewhere...

Lord Dalhousie, in a letter to Sir Login in January 1855, referred to his correspondence with the queen, regarding the much-speculated alliance between the princess and the maharaja:

...The Queen has again mentioned to me the Maharajah's second visit, and also alluded to the Coorg affair. I am glad to find that it promises well, and I hope may come to something, although, like other cases of 'true love' it may not always run smooth!

A few days later Sir Login asked Duleep Singh, 'Maharaja, what are your impressions about Princess Gowramma?'

Duleep Singh took a while to answer. 'She is an attractive girl. She speaks good English. She comes across as a good Christian. But I am not sure what kind of wife and mother she will make.'

He continued, 'I am not excited by arranged marriages. I would rather stay single if I am not able to find someone on my own who is suitable for me. In any case I am not in a hurry.' Sir Login did not press the subject further.

During August 1855, Lord Dalhousie was on an inspection of southern India, and camped at Kottegiri near the Nilgiris for several days. He had been desperate to find a place with mild weather to alleviate the excruciating pain in his leg. Even though he refused to admit it, it was suspected that he had gout. His overall health was also deteriorating rapidly.

While at Kottegiri, his ADC took permission to visit his brother in Coorg. On his assistant's return, Dalhousie was amused when told that the British residing in the isolated and remote Coorg believed that Britain was losing the Crimean War, and that the queen had taken refuge in India with her family!

Dalhousie was, however, happy that the economic condition of Coorg had improved with the introduction of scientific cultivation of coffee and spices. Some of the British planters from Ceylon had migrated to Coorg and started developing coffee estates for which the land and weather were ideal.

7

THE PRINCESS AND THE MAHARAJA

*T*HOUGH QUEEN VICTORIA and Prince Albert were preoccupied with affairs of the state and the war in the Crimea, they were eager to see the young Indian maharaja receive a more enduring foundation in Western education. Consequently, the Logins rented a large mansion in Wimbledon to create a conducive atmosphere for Duleep Singh to pursue his education. The Login couple moved in there along with their young son, Harry. Pundit Nehemiah Goreh, valet Thornton and the maharaja's retinue of servants also shifted to the mansion. A cook named Russell was hired to cater to the maharaja's increasing fondness for European food particularly steaks.

Since the maharaja was over-aged to attend a public school Sir Login took on the task of guiding him in his studies at home

Tutors were arranged to visit the residence to give lessons in mathematics and science. There were frequent visits to the Crystal Palace, the venue of 'The Great Exhibition' of 1851. Duleep Singh enjoyed these educational trips where he was exposed to the practical application of science. Within a year of their arrival at England, Duleep Singh had made satisfactory progress in his education. To round off his curriculum, he was taught to play a variety of musical instruments, the harmonium being one of his favourites.

The royal couple kept a close watch on Duleep Singh's progress. He was often invited to spend time at the palace with the royal children. On 26 January 1855, Duleep Singh was a special guest for dinner at Windsor Castle. He stayed on with the royal family, and returned to Wimbledon three days later after attending the divine service with the queen, Prince Albert and the couple's four older children, in the private chapel of the castle.

In the summer of 1855, the maharaja moved to another temporary accommodation at Ashburton House in Roehampton. In a surprising demonstration of magnanimity, the queen allowed Maharaja Duleep Singh and the Logins to use one of her large mansions in Kew, the Church House, so that her children, Duleep Singh and the other English royalty who lived in the nearby manors, could meet frequently. All the houses opened on to the Kew Gardens, which became a large playground for the royal children to romp in after the garden was closed to the public.

During Duleep Singh's stay at Kew, the Drummonds brought Princess Victoria Gowramma over a few times to encourage the latter to socialise with the royal children. There was, however, another reason behind the visits to Kew—as wished by the queen, it was to enable the two oriental bluebloods to get to know each other better. Everyone involved in the lives of the two young people placed in such a quaint position by fate, hoped that cupid would soon strike the maharaja and the princess.

Princess Gowramma enjoyed her time in London, meeting new people and attending court functions. She spent a few days with her father who was by then in the midst of an acrimonious lawsuit against the East India Company. The Company, however, was determined to go through the entire legal process to avoid making any payments. Fortunately for the raja, he continued to receive moral support from some of the liberals in England and the newspapers. Some of the members of the parliament continued to raise the issue of the Indian princes who had lost their kingdoms to the East India Company, and argued that adequate legal avenues be provided to the citizens of the colonies. There was outrage in certain sections of the British society at the lack of proper justice for the former rulers in India.

Three years had passed since Gowramma's arrival in England. With each passing day, she was becoming increasingly alienated from her family. The Drummonds made sure she did not spend much time with her father. By the middle of 1855, Veerarajendra and his party had moved to 20, Clifton Villas, on Warwick Road, Maida Hill West in Paddington. Though smaller, it was an elegant accommodation located on the banks of the picturesque Regent's Canal, popularly known as Little Venice. Veerarajendra and his household felt that their earlier residence did not bring them good luck. The problems created by Munshi Shantamalla and the hurdles that had cropped up in his case against the Company made the raja conclude that a change of residence would alter his fortunes.

The London sojourn was, however, not progressing too well for Mudduveeramma and Siddaveeramma, the raja's two women. They found themselves stifled by the sequestered life they were forced to endure for almost four years now. Having come prepared for a year, they yearned to go back to Benares. The only respite for Mudduveeramma came when a French artist was granted permission by Veerarajendra to prepare a portrait of his attractive wife. The sketch of the exotic bejewelled woman titled *Femme du Radja de Kourg,* was considered highly seductive by the people in London and Paris.

Princess Gowramma was by now totally out of touch with her mother-tongue. She found it more and more difficult to converse with her father and other members in the house. Her behaviour was more English than Indian. In spite of the indifferent attitude displayed by his daughter, Veerarajendra was still proud of his 'little pigeon'.

Much to the satisfaction of Her Majesty, Princess Gowramma showed marked improvements in her grooming and deportment. She, however, continued to lag behind in academics. She was self-assured, and conducted herself confidently in the company of British high society. Princess Gowramma was one of the important guests of the queen at Windsor Castle on 23 January 1856, for a state dinner. She was asked to stay on to witness a performance of Shakespeare's *Merchant of Venice*. Gowramma, familiar with the Bard's plays, enjoyed the show immensely in the company of the prince of Wales, Princess Royal and Princess Alice. She spent two carefree days with the royal children. The 'Court Circular' published in *The Times* highlights the prominence given to Princess Gowramma by Her Majesty:

COURT CIRCULAR.

WINDSOR, JAN. 25.

The Queen, accompanied by the Princess Royal, Princess Alice, and Princess Victoria Gauromma of Coorg, drove out this morning in an open carriage.

His Royal Highness Prince Albert went out shooting, accompanied by the Duke of Cambridge, General della Marmora, and Captain Drummond, R.N.

The Prince of Wales and Prince Alfred rode out on horseback, attended by Mr. Gibbs.

The following visitors left the Castle to-day,—the Earl and Countess of Shaftesbury and Lady Victoria Ashley, the Earl of Aberdeen, the Earl and Countess of Ellesmere and Lady Blanche Egerton, Sir George and Lady Grey, Viscount Torrington, Lord Churchill, and Admiral Sir Edmund Lyons.

General Alfonso della Marmora, commanding the Sardinian Contingent of the Allied Armies, was invested by Her Majesty on Thursday, in the Royal Closet, with the insignia of the Grand Cross of the Bath.

Mr. Cairns, M.P., and a deputation from the Chamber of Commerce of Belfast, consisting of Mr. John Herdman, Mr. Robert Hull, Mr. J. Preston, and Mr. T. M'Clure, had an interview with Lord Stanley of Alderley and the Right Hon. R. Lowe yesterday at the office of the Board of Trade.

Sir George Grey returned to town yesterday from a visit to the Queen at Windsor Castle.

Despatches for the Governors of Canada, the Mauritius, and Malta, were sent last evening from the Colonial-office.

As for Duleep Singh, he was engrossed in pursuing his education and acquiring the skills of an English nobleman. In accordance with the treaty with the British, he would 'come of age' at sixteen, and looked forward to higher allowances and a greater degree of freedom. However, the Board of Control of the East India Company decided to extend the age to eighteen years, citing the need for the maharaja to complete his education in England. Duleep Singh had also decided that he would think of marriage only after he was financially in a better position. Back in India, Maharani Jindan Kaur was deeply concerned that her son was still not married. She kept complaining to Jung Bahadur, 'My poor son should have had at least three wives and many children by now. The feringhees are ruining him, and our great family.'

Having widened his social circle, Duleep Singh expressed his desire to Sir Login to rent a large estate in Scotland where he could indulge in his favourite pastime of hunting and falconry. After obtaining clearances from the India Office, Sir Login managed to identify a property—Castle Menzies in Perthshire.

The maharaja's entourage moved to Castle Menzies from Kew by early spring. Inspired by the Scots, Duleep Singh took to wearing the Highlander's kilt, and endeared himself to the locals who started calling the handsome maharaja 'the black prince of Perthshire'. Prominent members of British society were frequent visitors to the sprawling estate, which was ideal for hunting. Duleep Singh derived the maximum pleasure from training his falcons, a trait Sir Login had frowned upon ever since their Fatehgarh days. In Sir Login's opinion, it was a cruel oriental sport. The doctor tried his best to divert the attention of the maharaja from falconry to what the English upper-class indulged in—grouse shooting. For his sixteenth birthday, the queen had presented him a shotgun, hoping her young friend would take to the more sophisticated sport. The Logins were convinced that 'there was naturally still underlying all a strain of indolence and indifference to suffering, which is innate in the Oriental, and which Western education only overcomes with difficulty.'

At Castle Menzies, Lady Login delivered her sixth child. The girl child was named Edith Dalhousie Login. Maharaja Duleep Singh insisted that he should be the godfather to the baby. The Logins, however, named the baby after Lord Dalhousie, thus partly fulfilling the promise made to the governor-general during his visit to Fatehgarh Park in 1851.

On 4 September 1856, Duleep celebrated his eagerly awaited eighteenth birthday. There was a festive atmosphere in Castle Menzies for the occasion. Gifts arrived from the queen, her children, and some of the prominent citizens in the neighbourhood. Duleep Singh was most touched by the present the queen and her consort had sent—a beautifully bound Bible in German, Prince Albert's mother-tongue. Duleep Singh was by then also learning German. The Drummonds and Princess Victoria Gowramma were invited for the birthday party. The Logins were delighted to see the two young royals quite at ease in each other's company. Though Duleep Singh had not appeared too impressed with Gowramma during their earlier meetings, he now wanted to know and understand her better. He found Gowramma to be highly influenced by English literature. She had become quite romantic, quoting poems from John Keats, Percy Bysshe Shelley, William Wordsworth, and the current sensation, poet laureate Alfred Tennyson.

The year 1856 was progressing well for Princess Gowramma. Her marble bust sculpted by Baron Carlo Marochetti, the queen's favourite sculptor, was reported in newspapers and widely discussed by art lovers for its perfection and uniqueness. Even though Gowramma had wanted to pose in European clothes, Marochetti insisted on her wearing the traditional Indian saree and blouse. She adorned herself with a beaded headdress and a crucifix around her neck. The bust was painted with watercolours and later gilded, giving the image a life-like appearance. An art critic of the time commented: 'Looking at the sculpture one can almost expect the eyelids to quiver.' Marochetti was successful in capturing the fine features, the dusky complexion and the attractive dark brown eyes of his subject. The sculpture was displayed at

Osborne House along with a similar bust of the maharaja (without colours) sculpted a few months earlier by Baron Marochetti.

Queen Victoria was protective of her two favourite Indian royalties, though both were quite obstinate at times. She made sure they were prominently mentioned in all the court circulars. The queen was aware of the shoddy treatment meted out to members of the royal families in India by the East India Company, and wanted to make amends in her own way.

Maharaja Duleep Singh had reached an important milestone in his life. There would be many significant events unfolding in the coming months, now that he had officially 'come of age'. The maharaja expected the East India Company to promptly honour the terms of the Lahore Treaty. He patiently waited a month for a response from the Company's office at East India House. When no communication was forthcoming, he made a representation to Sir Charles Wood, Secretary to the India Board. Still there was no reply. It became apparent that the Company was in no hurry to review his account in accordance with the treaty. On the other hand, a suggestion was floated to extend the coming of age from eighteen to twenty-one, as was applicable to everyone else in Britain at the time. The queen, who had a copy of his petition, was appalled at the evasiveness of the Company. There seemed to be a concerted effort by those at East India House to renege on the terms of the treaty.

After waiting for a few days, the queen wrote a persuasive letter to Lord Stanley, the president of the Board of Control, on October 1856:

The Queen has seen the Memorandum, which the Maharaja Duleep Singh has sent to the East India Company. She thinks all he asks very fair and reasonable, and she trusts that the

East India Company will be able to comply with them. As we are in complete possession since 1849 of the Maharaja's enormous and splendid kingdom, the Queen thinks we ought to do everything (which does not interfere with the safety of her Indian dominions) to render the position of this interesting and peculiarly good and amiable Prince as agreeable as possible, and not to let him have the feeling that he is a prisoner.

His being a Christian and completely European, (or rather more English) in his habits and feelings render this much more necessary and at the same time more easy.

The Queen has a very strong feeling that everything should be done to show respect and kindness towards these fallen Indian Princes, whose kingdoms we have taken from them, and who are naturally very sensitive to attention and kindness.

Amongst all these however the Maharaja stands to a certain degree alone, from his civilization and likewise from his having lost his kingdom when he was a child, entirely by the faults and deceits of others.

It was more than two years since Duleep Singh's arrival i England. He had made several friends amongst the royalty, countr squires and senior government officials. That he was favoure by Queen Victoria and members of her family was well know to the British public. Duleep Singh was unable to compreher that the officers of the British East India Company might depri him of his dues. In addition to his allowances, he wanted to free to travel and reside wherever he wished, without having get permission from India Office. He was officially an adult no He had spent two very happy years in England and had enjoy protocol at par with European princes. The unexpected indifferen of the East India Company towards him brought on a sense despondency in him. Duleep Singh hoped that the letter fro the queen would prompt the Company to honour the terms of the Treaty signed in 1849 at Lahore. He now realised how he had been tricked into signing away his entire kingdom to the British as an eleven-year-old maharaja. He reposed all his faith in Her Majesty and the fair play of the British. Still, he was deeply concerned after what he heard from the ex-raja of Coorg, who even after four years of struggle, was yet to receive repayment of his funds from the Company.

His worst fears came true when Lord Stanley handed over the entire issue to the government of India for a decision. The delaying tactics continued with letters and telegraphs being exchanged between London and Calcutta. The queen found herself helpless in alleviating the predicament faced by the maharaja. She continued to exert her influence but very little was achieved except polite letters from the Board of Control.

It began to slowly dawn on Duleep Singh that the British government and the officers of the East India Company were far from being his well-wishers and guardians. They had usurped enormous wealth and property from him. Now they were attempting to renege on their promises. In India, the rapaciousness with which Dalhousie annexed the kingdom of Satara and Oudh angered many rulers and their subjects. The highhanded actions of the governor-general in taking possession of several small kingdoms on one pretext or the other, shocked the liberal-minded citizens of Britain as well. There was a simmering discontent across the land, especially north of the Vindyas.

At the sitting of the House of Lords on 18 April 1856, many eminent members of parliament denounced Lord Dalhousie's doctrine of annexation of several kingdoms, especially the territory Oudh, on unprincipled grounds. One of the members, Sir E rry, said:

...The doctrine of annexation was unsound upon financial principles; but on the higher grounds of right and justice, and the obligations of every Christian Power, the House, he said, was called upon to interfere, and by its authority, check the system of territorial aggrandizement in India, which must tarnish the British name and weaken the foundation of British rule.

Another member, Mr Murrough, too strongly denounced the dealings of the government of India, especially with reference to the family of raja of Coorg. However, Sir James Weir-Hogg, chairman of the East India Company and a member of parliament strongly defended the actions of his Government. Outnumbered, the liberals were unable to influence the avaricious policies of the Company.

Queen Victoria and Prince Albert found Maharaja Duleep Singh deeply upset and distressed at the turn of events. They suggested a change of scene for the maharaja. They urged the Logins to take Duleep Singh and a few of his friends on a long tour of Europe; it would be educational as well as a well-deserved holiday. Sir and Lady Login made all the arrangements and the party left England for the Continent in December 1856. The maharaja's good friend Ronald Leslie-Melville accompanied him.

The queen was equally worried about her goddaughter, the fifteen-year-old Princess Victoria Gowramma. The Drummonds had informed the queen that the princess, though much improved, was not serious about pursuing her studies, and was lagging behind children younger to her. She suffered from an inferiority complex which made her behave annoyingly truant at times. Her health too was not vigorous. While she was happy meeting people, attending parties, concerts and balls, she disliked any serious application in learning new skills and acquiring knowledge. To boost h morale the queen invited Princess Gowramma to Buckingham Palace on 6 April 1856, to spend time with her children. She and Prince Albert hoped the princess would soon shed her 'eastern indolence', and start taking her education more seriously.

One of the highlights of this period for Princess Victoria Gowramma was an invitation to a Royal Juvenile Ball in the Throne Room of Buckingham Palace on 25 April 1856. Mrs Drummond chaperoned the star-struck princess. There were 276 guests, including young European princes, princesses and sons and daughters of the nobility. It was an unforgettable evening for the princess from Coorg. She relished every moment as she danced and waltzed with many handsome princes. She promptly fell in love with most of them! *The Times, London* carried the following 'Court Circular' released from the Palace:

ROYAL JUVENILE BALL.

(From the *Court Circular*.)

Her Majesty gave a juvenile ball last evening. Invitations were issued to a party of 276.

Her Royal Highness the Duchess of Kent arrived at Buckingham Palace at 9 o'clock, attended by Lady Fanny Howard, the Baroness de Speth, and Lord James Murray.

Their Royal Highnesses the Duchess of Cambridge and the Princess Mary were attended by Lady Geraldine Somerset and Major Home Purves.

His Royal Highness the Duke of Cambridge was attended by Colonel the Hon. James Macdonald.

The Royal family were conducted to the White Drawing-room, where the Queen received her illustrious guests.

His Serene Highness Prince Edward of Saxe-Weimar and the Countess of Dornburg and the Princess Gauromma of Coorg were present.

The general company began to arrive about a-quarter before 9 o'clock, and were ushered into the Picture Gallery.

Her Majesty and Prince Albert, with the Prince of Wales, the Princess Royal, Prince Alfred, Prince Arthur, the Princess Alice, the Princess Helena, the Princess Louisa, the Duchess of Kent, the Duchess of Cambridge, and the Princess Mary, and the Duke of Cambridge, entered the Throne-room, which was prepared for dancing, soon after 9 o'clock, and were followed by the nobility and gentry, with the sons and daughters of their respective families.

Back in Edinburgh, the Drummonds found it difficult to control the princess who could not get over the Juvenile Ball. The romantic princess, feeling lonely and depressed, easily fell in love with any young man she met. Major Drummond, an ex-cavalry officer, maintained a stable in the sprawling estate. One of the stable boys who took Princess Gowramma and the Drummonds' daughters riding in the estate, got romantically involved with the princess. The princess and the groom exchanged glances, wrote letters to each other and had secret rendezvous, all of which progressed unnoticed by the Drummonds for quite a while.

The Drummonds were initially happy to see Gowramma's enthusiasm in horse-riding and outdoor activities. They were pleased to see their otherwise sullen ward looking vivacious and happy, till the day they discovered the lovesick princess in the arms of the stable boy. The entire incidence became quite a scandal in the neighbourhood, and the news soon reached the ears of the queen.

The queen, pregnant at the time with her ninth child, was quite upset. She advised the Drummonds to shift Gowramma out of Edinburgh. She suggested moving to the Isle of Wight so that the princess's health too could benefit from the proximity to the sea. The queen was genuinely fond of her goddaughter and wanted her to be happy. Her Majesty was now not only concerned about the princess's poor health but also her behaviour. The queen was quite troubled to notice traits of a *femme fatale* in the oriental princess.

The next visit of Princess Gowramma to London was during the last week of May 1856. She spent some time with her father at Clifton Villas. Her stepmother Mudduveeramma had prepared some of her favourite Indian dishes, which she now found very spicy. On 31 May, she represented her father at the foundation laying ceremony of the 'Home in London for Oriental Strangers' where Prince Albert was the Chief Guest. Veerarajendra, who was indisposed, could not attend the function. Maharaja Duleep Singh was one of the speakers on the occasion, and contributed 500 pound sterling to the lodging house, which would provide temporary accommodation for visitors from India, Arabia, Africa, China, the Straits of Malacca, the Mozambique and the Island of South Pacific.

Around this time, Lord Dalhousie reached England, having retired as the governor-general of India. Veerarajendra took it on himself to write a congratulatory letter to Dalhousie, hoping to garner his support in the case against the Company. In his letter dated 22 May 1856, he praised Lord Dalhousie for his contributions to the overall development of India. He expressed his gratitude for permitting him and his daughter to come to England where the little princess, under Her Majesty's patronage had gained immensely after her conversion. Lord Dalhousie was in poor health and had been diagnosed with cancer. While concluding his letter, Veerarajendra requested for an interview with the former governor-general:

> ...Fearful of trespassing too long upon your lordship's attention, I shall now conclude with the humble but earnest request, that, so soon as your lordship is sufficiently recovered, I may be allowed the honour of paying my respects and thanks to you in a personal interview—an interview which will be but the renewal of an acquaintance that commenced in 1849. It will, doubtless be in your lordship's recollection, that in the above year, when your lordship was on your way from northwestern

provinces to Calcutta, myself and daughter [Gowramma] had the honour of dining with your lordship at the house of Colonel Macgregor, at Benares, and I beg to assure your lordship that your kindness and affability to me upon that occasion will never be obliterated from my mind...

Lord Dalhousie replied on 2 June 1856, and was unambiguous in expressing his dislike for the raja of Coorg:

Lord Dalhousie presents his compliments to His Highness Veer Rajundur Wadeer, ex-Rajah of Coorg in reply to the letter which he has received, dated 22 May; he begs to state that he declines the interview which the Rajah requests.

Lord Dalhousie further begs to add, that, in the event of their meeting elsewhere, he must decline to recognize any acquaintance with the ex-Rajah of Coorg.

Veerarajendra, very much offended, wrote back to Dalhousie on 9 June, expressing his surprise at such an insulting response from his lordship:

...As your lordship may readily conceive, I have found, by melancholy experience, how little sympathy attends misfortune; but it appears I had yet to learn that mine could ever have been considered, by one of your lordship's exalted station, as a butt for unprovoked, unfeeling, and deliberate insult...

Dr Jeaffreson, who was in London at the time, had helped Veerarajendra in drafting these letters to Lord Dalhousie. He continued to assist and guide the raja in his quest for justice.

Prior to this exchange of letters between Lord Dalhousie and Veerarajendra, the Court of Directors of the East India Company met on 14 May 1856 to decide on the pension for the retired governor-general who had contributed immensely in expanding their influence in India. After much deliberation, the annual pension for Dalhousie was fixed at 5,000 pound sterling. Lord Dalhousie fretted in private that the 'rascally raja of Coorg' got more pension than what was decided for him!

With help from Dr Jeaffreson, Veerarajendra's request to remain in England to pursue his case against the East India Company was discussed in the House of Commons on 25 July 1856. The marquess of Clanricarde and the duke of Argyll argued that the raja of Coorg, whose family had been allies of the Company for many years, should be allowed to remain in the country to pursue the lawsuit. The Company's assertion that the raja was a state prisoner and had permission to be in England only for a year was overruled.

Queen Victoria and Prince Albert were anxious to bring about an alliance between Maharaja Duleep Singh and Princess Gowramma as soon as possible. By the end of 1856, they felt it was time to raise the subject directly with Duleep Singh. They invited the young maharaja to Osborne to spend a few days with them. Prince Albert had lengthy discussions with the young maharaja, but his response was disappointing. In her diary on 14 December 1856, the queen made the following notings:

> ...Albert spoke of our idea regarding Gouramma, to which he replied that he could not marry her, that he liked her very much, thought her a very nice little girl, whom he would like as a friend but not as a wife. She did not at all come up to his idea of a person he could marry. He must have time, and he wished to see the world. Albert told him he must beware of designing mothers, who might try to catch him, and if he lost

heart, it might be too late. He replied that he was also quite aware of this. Poor boy, I feel so much for him for he is so good and so well principled. But I am sorry about Gouramma, who I know would wish to marry him...

Mrs Drummond brought Princess Gowramma to London during the beginning of February 1857. It was nearly a year since her last visit to London. After meeting her father at Clifton Villas, Mrs Drummond took Gowramma to visit the royal family at Windsor Castle on 4 February. The princess was invited to spend two days at the castle with the royal children, especially Princess Alice. Queen Victoria and Prince Albert were happy to see the sixteen-year-old Princess Gowramma looking attractive and elegantly turned out. They advised her to concentrate on her studies and be a good Christian. In accordance with the queen's wishes, the Drummonds relocated to a seaside manor in Ryde on the northeastern coast of Isle of wight. Whenever the queen and Prince Albert spent time at Osborne House, they invited Princess Gowramma over to their Italianate palazzo.

The ninth and last child of Queen Victoria and Prince Albert—Princess Beatrice—was born on 14 April 1857. Though fond of her large brood, the queen disliked pregnancy and childbirth. She confided in Princess Royal, her eldest daughter that giving birth was not an elegant process and made her feel like a cow! The day after the birth of Princess Beatrice, Princess Gowramma visited the queen at Buckingham Palace along with Mrs Drummond. Veerarajendra called on the royal family on 17 April 1857 to enquire about the health of the queen and the infant princess.

The relatively even progression of life in London received jolt with the incident of the Sepoy Mutiny in faraway India. The event that took place in the northern city of Meerut, on 10 May 1857, shook the foundation of the British Raj. The Indian soldiers revolted against the British, with Hindus and Muslims joining hands to overthrow the white rulers. The use of the new Enfield guns and the controversial greased cartridges, provided the spark for the revolt. The highhanded actions of Lord Dalhousie, who had retired a year earlier, had also created deep discontentment among the Indians.

The Hindus and Muslims viewed the increased activities of the evangelists in the country with suspicion. Taking the cue from Meerut, there was spontaneous uprising all over north India. Indians in most parts of the country rallied behind Bahadur Shah Zafar, the last Mughal emperor, and the movement soon turned into a cry for independence. The British were taken unawares and suffered heavy casualties. It was finally the lack of a centralised leadership and strategy that led to the Indians being overpowered by the British. Fortunately for the British, the telegraph system established by Dalhousie saved the day. With quick means of communication, they were able to forewarn other centres. John Lawrence received the last telegraphic message of the uprising in Lahore, moments before the sepoys severed the cables. John Lawrence moved to Delhi with a strong contingent of loyal Jat Sikhs, the former subjects of Maharaja Duleep Singh. After months of siege, the British eventually captured the stronghold of the rebels. John Lawrence's brother, Sir Henry Lawrence, the newly appointed Resident at Lucknow, was in serious trouble with the rebels besieging the residency.

Maharaja Duleep Singh and his friend Ronald Leslie-Meville were holidaying in Geneva when the news of the revolt reached them. Days later, they received more details of the uprising.

Many friends and acquaintances of Duleep Singh in India were severely affected. Sir Henry Lawrence, whom Duleep Singh knew from his Lahore days, had lost his life to a stray bullet during the siege of the Lucknow Residency. He was anguished to hear that his boyhood friend, Tommy Scott, who had joined the army had lost his mother, brother and sister in the violence unleashed on the British in Lucknow. Duleep Singh's mansion at Fatehgarh was ransacked, and the caretaker, Sergeant Elliot, his tutor Walter Guise and their families along with many others, had tried to escape in boats to Kanpur. But the nearly two hundred British men, women and children were massacred as they reached Kanpur. Bhajan Lal survived the attack, and did all he could to retrieve some of the maharaja's possessions at Fatehgarh Park. The American Presbyterian Christian Mission at Fatehgarh was also not spared.

In England, Maharaja Duleep Singh and Veerarajendra became targets of criticism by a section of the British society. It was generally felt that these two former rulers were not expressing sufficient regret at the slaughter of innocent British men, women and children in India. Even Sir Login found the maharaja reluctant in showing his outrage at the atrocities against the British and Christians in India. However, the British fought back to regain their lost strongholds, and the tide soon turned. The reprisal on the mutineers was horrendous to the extent that many in Britain were appalled at the brutalities committed by the British soldiers. Lord Dalhousie, now retired, had to acknowledge that it was with the help of the much-criticised Jung Bahadur of Nepal that the British were able to recapture Lucknow in early 1858. Ironically, it was the subjects of the exiled Maharaja Duleep Singh and Jung Bahadur, the son-in-law of the banished raja of

Coorg, who rendered crucial help to the British in fighting and subduing the rebels.

Away from the turmoil in her homeland, Victoria Gowramma was more cheerful after their shift to Ryde from the bleak weather of Edinburgh. She heard of the revolt in India from the Drummonds. Mrs Drummond hoped the princess would show outrage but Gowramma remained apathetic. In the five years of living in England, her alienation from India was total. There was barely any sign of attachment to her country or her relatives back home. Except for occasionally remembering her half-sister Gangamma and foster mother Subadhramma, she was happy to have moved away from the noisy environs of Benares. Her meeting with her father too had become less frequent. She looked forward to visits to Osborne House and other palaces and meeting the British aristocracy. Gowramma was by then well acquainted with all the princes and princesses. She exchanged letters with Princess Alice frequently. All that Gowramma secretly craved for were elegant parties, banquets, queen's drawing-room get-togethers, musical concerts, and men's attention.

Whilst the revolt in India was spreading across the northern parts of the subcontinent, the Royal Literary Fund invited Veerarajendra and the prince of Oudh for the 68th anniversary festival of the fund, held on 19 May 1857, at the Free Masons' Tavern. Amongst the prominent invitees were Dr David Livingstone and Thomas Babington Macaulay. There was an interesting discussion on Literature of the Colonies'.

Even though the uprising had engulfed the entire north, it did not significantly influence the southern parts of India. In Coorg, the locals showed their solidarity to the British. After the rebellion was suppressed, the administration of India was brought under the Crown. The chief commissioner of Mysore and Coorg, Sir Mark Cubbon, by then a major general and also knighted, issued a notification on 26 February 1861 exempting the 'gallant people of Coorg' from the Disarming Act which was introduced all over British India.

Veerarajendra's hope of recovering the proceeds of the investment from the East India Company was kept alive with the fragile support from the liberals in the House of Commons. He continued to receive invitations from the queen to attend formal ceremonies in the palaces, which boosted his sagging morale. Repeated efforts of the India Office to send him back to India were stalled by the members of the House of Commons, as the case was still pending disposal at the Chancery Court. The Government of India constantly tried to sabotage the case by bringing in various reasons and charges of atrocities committed by Veerarajendra during his reign. They projected their defense in the case as 'confiscation' of the raja's land and property following his dethronement in 1834 on request from his persecuted close relatives, dewans and subjects. The wealth of his former kingdom, they said, was being utilised for the well-being of the people. They emphasised that Veerarajendra was being compensated with a handsome pension.

Dr William Jeaffreson was annoyed at the hurdles the East India Company was introducing at every step of the case. He decided to publish a book to paint Veerarajendra as a benevolent ruler whom his former subjects had respected and loved. His book, *Coorg and Its Rajahs*, was published in late 1857. However Dr Jeaffreson wished to remain anonymous, and the author of the book was mentioned as 'An Officer formerly in the service of Veerarajendra Wodeer, Rajah of Coorg.'

The book was dedicated to Veerarajendra:

DEDICATION

TO HIS HIGHNESS VEER RAJUNDER WADEER,
RAJAH OF COORG

Honoured Prince,

Having, ere the 'evil day' had arrived, received from Your Highness many proofs of kindness, condescension, and generosity, I beg permission to dedicate the following narrative to you, not only as a mark of my sincere gratitude, but also as a token of my admiration to the philosophic fortitude and dignified patience with which your Highness has borne alike the wrongs of the oppressor and the aspersions of the slander.

I have the honour to be,

Honoured Prince,

Your Highness's Most Obedient and Most Grateful Servant,

THE AUTHOR

The concluding paragraph of the book reads as follows:

Our little narrative being now brought to a conclusion, the writer may be allowed to observe, that the objects of his works will be sufficiently attained, if, in addition to affording amusement and information, it shall cause the policy and acts of the Honourable East India Company to be watched with a more vigilant eye than heretofore, and shall awaken in the public mind a sympathy on behalf of the last of the Coorg Rajahs, His Highness Veer Rajundur Wadeer – A Man More sinn'd against, than sinning.

Sadly, for Veerarajendra and his friend Dr Jeaffreson, the book failed to evoke reaction of any great advantage to influence the course of the legal battle the raja was fighting against the Company.

A few days after their arrival at Ryde, Gowramma developed chest congestion and a persistent cough. One day she expectorated blood. She, however, did not bring this to the notice of her guardians, assuming it to be just another process of growing up. After spending a few weeks in their new abode by the seaside, she felt better and the symptoms subsided. The relatively warmer environment of the Isle of Wight suited Gowramma, and her health subsequently showed marked improvement.

Her Majesty's grand plan of a matrimonial alliance with Maharaja Duleep Singh rapidly fading, the queen was anxious to find a suitable husband for the vulnerable Indian princess. She seriously considered finding a match for Gowramma from amongst the European aristocracy. With the queen now keeping a close watch on Gowramma, the Drummonds too took extra care to provide all the comforts for the princess. In addition, they had to be vigilant as the young princess showed an increasing tendency to indulge in frequent flirtations. Her interest in education continued to be lackadaisical. The Drummonds attributed the development of the character of the Indian princess to 'native instinct for duplicity and intrigue.' Possibilities of a union between Duleep Singh and Gowramma were still not totally ruled out.

Similar arguments of 'native tendency for duplicity' were used by the India Office to justify their actions in depriving Maharaja Duleep Singh of his allowances and freedom to manage his own affairs, which were promised to him on attaining the age of eighteen. With Queen Victoria actively pursuing the early settlement of Duleep Singh's claims, the Court of Directors of the East India Company finally agreed on 29 December 1857 that the maharaja, already nineteen-year-old, was free from any restraints and was no longer under the guardianship of Sir John Login and Lady Lena Login. However, the more important issue of the enhanced allowances was not addressed.

The high-spirited Duleep Singh was in a hurry to enjoy his newly-found freedom. He immediately decided on indulging in two of his favourite activities—hunting and hawking. He planned a trip by himself to the island of Sardinia where he was told that herds of wild boars roamed the countryside and the terrain was also suitable for training his falcons. Another reason was to get away from the cold and bleak weather in England. The queen was concerned that the young maharaja was planning to travel alone without the supervision of Sir Login. While she was happy that her young ward was 'trying out his wings', she recommended that he take an ADC along. The queen invited Duleep Singh to the Palace on two occasions, before he finally set out to Sardinia on 2 March 1858. In deference to Her Majesty's wishes, Duleep Singh took one Dr Parson as his aide. He had a small entourage to handle his hunting equipment and the falcons.

By the beginning of 1858, the Drummonds had grown tired of looking after the recalcitrant Gowramma. It had been six years since they had assumed the charge of the princess and their growing daughters now needed their attention. The queen, on the Drummonds' request, agreed to relieve them of the responsibilities, and find another guardian for the young princess. The queen thought of Sir Login and his wife Lena, who had handled well the affairs of Maharaja Duleep Singh. The Logins had plenty of free time since they were no longer the official guardians of the twenty-year-old maharaja. Queen Victoria felt that the kindly Lady Lena Login would make an excellent surrogate mother for

Princess Gowramma who needed gentle care and handling. Though initially reluctant to take on the responsibility, Lady Login finally agreed to be the guardian of the seventeen-year-old princess. The queen had not given up her dream project of bringing about a union between Duleep Singh and Gowramma. 'If at all there is anyone who can make this matrimonial alliance possible, it is you my Lady Login,' the queen had said.

In accordance with the instructions from the queen, Mrs Drummond brought Princess Victoria Gowramma on 6 September 1858, from the Isle of Wight to Albany Villas at Brighton, where the Logins had rented a house. Lady Login had met the princess on several occasions earlier. The Logins were also well acquainted with her father Veerarajendra. Gowramma appeared particularly happy to be moving in with the Logins, having had enough of the monotonous life with the Drummonds in the country. The queen had instructed her staff to arrange for a house in Kew for the Logins and Princess Gowramma. A house similar to the one where the Logins had lived with Maharaja Duleep Singh was soon identified and renovated for their use.

The queen wanted Lady Lena Login to write as often as possible, giving details of her goddaughter's progress. The queen also wanted Lady Login to find out the circumstances leading to the scandalous behaviour of Gowramma during her stay with the Drummonds. After a few days, Lady Login gently brought up the delicate issue. To Lady Login's surprise, Princess Gowramma opened her heart to her and was quite candid about the unfortunate incident. She said: 'The Drummonds were good to me, but it was only serious studies all the time. I desperately wanted to make more friends and enjoy the outdoors. In this attempt, I got into some bad company. I am sorry, I beg Her Majesty to pardon my indiscretions.'

By the time Duleep Singh returned from his rather unsuccessful hunting trip to Sardinia, Sir Login had negotiated the lease of an estate named Mulgrave in Yorkshire, which had a large area, well-populated with grouse and other game. In addition, he had rented a costly lodge at Auchlyne on Lock Tay. With the East India Company not releasing the allowances promised to him, Duleep Singh was finding it difficult to maintain his expensive lifestyle. Around this time, he made friends with the flamboyant Samuel Baker, a keen hunter and sportsman. Together they planned an elaborate shooting expedition the following year that would take them through Hungary, Transylvania, down the Danube, and finally to Constantinople. Duleep Singh wanted to get away from the depressing weather in England. At Mulgrave, he threw extravagant parties and invited notable personalities from British society; guests at Mulgrave included Veerarajendra and his daughter Princess Gowramma.

The queen was quite concerned about the future of Princess Gowramma. She looked upon the princess as more than a goddaughter. She was genuinely fond of the girl and wanted Lady Login to do all she could to prevent any embarrassing incident. The queen suggested a short visit to the Continent so that Lady Login could interest the princess with new scenes and ideas. On instructions from Her Majesty, the monthly allowance of 400 rupees for the princess was made for life by the government of India.

The queen now felt that a marriage alliance with a foreign prince or a nobleman might be the best option for Gowramma. She instructed Lady Login to arrange for the princess to meet some of the eligible young men during their proposed stay in Europe. The queen wanted Lady Login to inform her immediately if any mutual attachment between the princess and an eligible young man was noticed so that she could give her approval, provided the gentleman's position and character were credible. The motherly affection bestowed by Queen Victoria on her Indian goddaughter Princess Gowramma, and the young Maharaja Duleep Singh, amazed British society.

8

ROMAN HOLIDAY

*L*ADY LOGIN WAS in the midst of planning a tour of the Continent with Princess Victoria Gowramma, as desired by Her Majesty, when a serious problem surfaced. Within a few weeks of the princess moving in with them, Lady Login found her suffering from a relentless cough. A few days later, she noticed that Gowramma's handkerchief was stained with blood. Alarmed, she had the seventeen-year-old princess thoroughly checked by Dr Edward Ormerod of Brighton. The prognosis by the doctor was not good. Gowramma then confided that she had similar episodes while at Ryde with the Drummonds, but had never mentioned it and the symptoms too had soon disappeared. Lady Login immediately wrote to the queen, who urged Lady Login to take the princess to the southern part of the Continent that was closer to the seaside so that her chest infection could heal faster in the warmer climate. Gowramma was started on medication for tuberculosis—the dreaded disease for which no effective cure had yet been discovered.

By the end of the year, the princess recovered satisfactorily and her symptoms of consumption almost disappeared. The royal couple, despite their preoccupations, kept a close watch on Gowramma. They wanted the Logins to move to Europe with the princess, before the onset of winter in England. The Logins, however, requested the queen for more time. Being devout Christians, they sought permission to arrange for the confirmation of Princess Gowramma as a member of the Church of England. The princess was now seventeen years old, and it was six years since her baptism. The Logins were of the opinion that the act of confirmation would lift the princess out of her indolent disposition. Furthermore, they wanted some time to settle their older children in the house at Kew provided by the queen, and arrange for their education during their absence. The Logins wanted the confirmation to be held quietly at Brighton, along with other young boys and girls. In their opinion, the pomp and publicity given to Gowramma's baptism had taken away the religious solemnity of the event. The Logins arranged for the princess to receive advanced instructions in the scriptures from Reverend Vaughan Elliott at Brighton. They planned for the rite of confirmation to be administered by the Bishop of Winchester.

When the Logins informed the queen of their plans for Gowramma's confirmation, they were surprised at the reaction. The queen wanted the ceremony to be held at the Royal Church at Kew. She insisted that Gowramma's should be a 'private confirmation' and that the princess should be the only candidate to receive the Apostolic 'laying on of hands'. The queen also instructed that the archbishop of Canterbury, who had baptised the Princess in 1852, perform the rites of confirmation. It became clear to the Logins that this ceremony too would be more of a social event than a religious one. The queen wanted to make it a formal occasion to present her goddaughter, the confirmed Christian Princess from India, to British society.

On the Logins' request, Reverend Elliott had drawn up an elaborate programme for educating Princess Gowramma in the finer aspects of Christianity. The questions and answers forming the transcript of religious instructions for Gowramma were sent to the queen for her opinion. The queen, surprisingly, felt that the material was unduly searching and comprehensive. On Her Majesty's instructions, the process was simplified. Princess Gowramma, thus, spent the next few months preparing for the rituals and tests she would have to face for her confirmation.

The confirmation was finally held at the Royal Church at Kew on 10 January 1859. The archbishop of Canterbury, however, opined that the bishop of Winchester, as the Diocesan, was the appropriate person for administering the rites of confirmation. To her regret, the queen could not attend the ceremony because of an important engagement in Court. She asked Viscountess Hardinge, and Sir James Weir-Hogg to represent her. Both of them had been sponsors of the princess during her baptism in 1852. Sir James Weir-Hogg was also the godfather and the legal guardian of Princess Gowramma in his capacity as the chairman of the East India Company. Many friends and members of the congregation were invited. One of the prominent guests was Princess Gowramma's father, Veerarajendra.

On the day of the ceremony, just as the guests and members of the congregation were about to enter the church, a messenger in royal livery came from Windsor Castle, rushing on horseback. He handed over a parcel from Her Majesty, the queen, addressed to Lady Lena Login. The parcel contained a beautiful set of coral and diamond necklace with matching earrings, a gift from Her Majesty to Princess Gowramma. Lady Login was taken aback—months earlier, the queen had asked her to suggest a suitable gift and she had recommended that an ornate devotional book would be appropriate to remind the princess of the solemn occasion.

There was a message from the queen to Lady Login, written on Her Majesty's instructions by Sir Charles Phipps:

Dear Lady Login,

I send to you by the Queen's command, a present from Her Majesty to Princess Gouramma, upon the occasion of her confirmation.

The Queen hopes that these ornaments, instead of gratifying the vanity of the young Princess, may serve, when she looks at them, frequently to remind her of the high duties and responsibilities, which she has this day taken upon her.

The Queen is pleased to believe that your young charge feels deep affection and gratitude to Her Majesty, and that this feeling will be a constant motive to her, so to conduct herself as to justify the continued regard and protection of Her Majesty. But, the Queen hopes that, from this day, the Princess will feel the far higher, and holier aspirations, which should fill her soul with the desire to please that Almighty Being, whose service she this day takes upon her. And, before Whom the Queen, and the Princess, will equally have to answer for the part which they have each taken, in obtaining for the latter the blessed hopes of Christianity.

The Queen directs me to send many messages of kindness to the Princess, and to assure her that it gives Her Majesty sincere pleasure when you are able to give a satisfactory report of her.

Sincerely yours,

C.B. Phipps

Veerarajendra was overjoyed at the display of Her Majesty's affection towards his daughter. Dressed in fine silks and wearing on his person a great deal of 'barbaric jewellery', as the newspapers regularly described, the raja openly displayed his delight. He preened and posed in front of all the guests and photographers. He insisted on a dramatic photograph of himself standing with his eyes raised heavenwards in 'pious invocation' while his outstretched hands pointed to his daughter seated next to him with her eyes downcast. This was to epitomise a father's anguish in handing over his child to the care of the British!

Veerarajendra welcomed Lady Login's appointment as the new guardian of Gowramma. His dreams for his favourite daughter had indeed worked very well. He felt optimistic that his case against the East India Company would soon be resolved and that he could return to India with a large sum of money. Veerarajendra once again sought Sir John Login's help and advice with the case. In addition, he now entertained a desire for his sons to come to England and acquire Western education.

While Veerarajendra continued to be very fond of his daughter, Gowramma did not reciprocate his affection. The more anglicised she got, the more indifferent she was to her father. With her fluency in her mother tongue, Kannada, having considerably diminished, and the raja's knowledge of English being limited, they could no longer converse freely with each other.

Lady Lena Login wrote back to Sir Phipps, giving details of the confirmation ceremony. She wrote acknowledging the anxiety of the queen since 'the princess's future conduct would exercise a great influence for good or for evil on the females of India.' Lady Login assured in her letter, 'With God's help I am anxious to do my part in endeavouring to train her in such a way as to do credit to her Christian profession. Should the result of our experimental tour on the Continent be such as to lead the queen to desire that a prolonged residence should be made, we shall endeavour, at any personal inconvenience, to meet Her Majesty's wishes, if we can find suitable place where we can take our children.' Lady Login's youngest child, Mabel, was born in April 1858. She could not take the baby on the extended journey, and had to arrange to leave the child in the care of relatives. The Logins had already admitted their second daughter in a boarding school in Brighton. They decided that their eldest daughter, also named Lena, should accompany them to the Continent. Sir John Login agreed to go with his wife, though reluctantly, since he was keen to take up an assignment with the government of India, being placed directly under British administration since the revolt of 1857.

Living with the caring and affectionate Login couple made Princess Gowramma soon recover her spirits. She got on well with their daughter Lena, who was three years younger to her. However, she lagged behind the younger girl in learning. It was with difficulty that Gowramma was able to concentrate, be it lessons, music, drawing or painting. In spite of her fluency in speaking English, it was with great effort that she was able to read. She pestered those around her to read books and poetry to her. She accepted her shortcomings, but tried her best to please Lady Login and Sir Login.

Gowramma's health too showed marked improvement and she enjoyed horse-riding. Involvement in all the social activities kept her in a better frame of mind. She looked forward to invitations from the queen to attend grand events in the palaces. Princess Victoria Gowramma had emerged a favourite of the London newspapers who regularly recorded her attendance at various court functions in the company of the royal family.

On 15 November 1858, Lady Login sought an audience with the queen to get her guidance and instructions for the proposed excursion to the Continent with Princess Gowramma. The queen's instructions were clear—'Inculcate Christian values in Gowramma. Let the princess gain intellectually from her exposure to the magnificent civilization of Europe. And, the bracing weather and the sea breeze should clear her lungs, and improve her overall health.'

The Logins started making plans for their elaborate travel to various parts of Europe. They would, however, spend more time in Rome. By the time all the arrangements were in place, it was January 1859. Lady Login wanted to have a final interview with the queen before setting out on their journey. A request was made for an appointment through Sir Phipps. The queen promptly invited Lady Login and Princess Gowramma to Buckingham Palace to meet her and have lunch with the royal family on 27 January 1859. The day turned out to be a memorable one for the queen and her guests.

It was a private lunch where only the queen, Prince Albert and the royal children were present. The queen made her goddaughter feel at home. She asked Gowramma about her studies and her plans for the forthcoming tour of Europe. Gowramma spoke confidently and answered all the queries quite candidly. She assured the queen that she would work hard to improve her knowledge of various subjects and activities. She told her godmother that she would be learning French. The queen quipped: 'when I meet you next, I want you to *parlez le français très bien!*' After lunch, the queen took Lady Login aside for a tête-à-tête, and instructed Lady Login to keep the princess in Europe as long as necessary for her to regain her health. The queen also nurtured hopes that Maharaja Duleep Singh would soon find the much-improved Princess Gowramma suitable as his life partner.

It was late in the afternoon by the time Lady Login and Princess Gowramma took leave of the queen. One of Sir Charles Phipps' assistants came to escort Lady Login and Princess Gowramma out of the place. They were passing through some of the magnificent galleries and spectacular interiors, when one of the high doors was suddenly flung open to announce the arrival of the queen. The queen was excited and in great hurry. In her hand, she held aloft a telegraph, and seeing Lady Login, the queen called out quite uncharacteristically for the sovereign: 'Lady Login! Lady Login! I am a grandmother!'

Both Lady Login and Princess Gowramma curtsied and congratulated the ecstatic queen, thrilled to receive the news even before Prince Albert. This grandchild of the queen was the future Kaiser Wilhelm II of Germany. For the next few days, Lady Login and Princess Gowramma could not stop recounting their experience in Buckingham Palace.

The day after their memorable meeting with the queen Dr Login and Lady Lena Login, Princess Victoria Gowramma along with the Logins' daughter Lena, set out for Europe.

was a leisurely journey and they stopped at important cities. Buckingham Palace had provided them letters of introduction to British Ambassadors and other prominent individuals in various parts of the Continent. The Logins were already familiar with many nobles, whose acquaintance they had made during their earlier visit in 1856 along with Maharaja Duleep Singh. The British envoys received them with all the protocol due to a princess and her companions.

They spent a few days in Paris, exploring the various historical places. The visit to the Notre Dame Cathedral was one of the highlights of their stopover in the French capital. They travelled south by horse carriages along the ancient road via Francigena, which stretched from Canterbury to Rome. Princess Gowramma was enthralled as they went through the route taken by Christian pilgrims for centuries. Along the way, they broke journey at various French towns and villages and the princess got her first taste of the French language. The next destination was Geneva, where they planned a longer sojourn. They stayed close to Lake Geneva, enjoying long walks along the scenic waterfront. Their next extended stopover was Italy, where Gowramma was mesmerised by the Gothic architecture of Milan's Cathedral Duomo, one of the largest churches in the world.

En route, they visited Venice, Florence, Pisa, San Gimignano, Siena, Assisi, and finally reached Rome by the first week of March. The warm weather in Rome came as a great relief to Gowramma and she breathed without discomfort. She instantly fell in love with the balmy weather, the spectacular monuments, the friendly people and the food in Rome. Within days, she got the colour back on her otherwise pallid cheeks. The entire journey proved to be a happy experience for the Logins and the princess. The

Logins rented an apartment at 56, Capo la Casa, not too far from the Spanish Steps and the magnificent fountains sculpted by the famous Baroque sculptor, Giovanni Lorenzo Bernini. It was close to where the romantic poet John Keats lived decades earlier, and where Percy Bysshe Shelley and Lord Byron were frequent visitors to comfort their friend dying of consumption.

To the Login's great surprise, they found Maharaja Duleep Singh staying in Rome. He had cut short his hunting expedition with Samuel Baker, which had turned out be a fiasco. The Logins were delighted at the unexpected arrival of the maharaja and wondered whether it was the presence of Princess Gowramma that had drawn the maharaja to Rome.

The affection showered on Princess Gowramma by the Logins had lifted her sagging spirits. Breathing the warm Mediterranean air seemed to cure her of all her ailments. Gowramma was approaching her eighteenth birthday and was conscious of her exotic looks attracting attention wherever she went. She was a little disappointed that Duleep Singh, who visited them frequently, did not exude much tenderness towards her, despite the Logins' subtle allusion to an impending marriage proposal from the maharaja. Gowramma, however, was more attracted to the European aristocracy, and fantasised one of them whisking her away to their castle on a hill.

After days of travelling, the Logins now turned their attention to Gowramma's education in right earnest. A Parisian lady was engaged to teach her French, and an English instructor was engaged to guide the princess in painting and drawing. The Login's sixteen-year-old son, Edwy, joined them from Eton and his visit further brightened up the atmosphere at 56, Capo la Casa where the Logins had taken up residence. Princess Gowramma began to enjoy her stay in Rome. She loved to indulge in frequent rides in horse carriages through the streets of Rome. There were visits to the Vatican, the Coliseum, the Roman Forum, and other places of historic importance. She enjoyed walks with the Logins, especially to the Spanish Steps, where many people gathered in the evenings. Her favourite spot was the nearby Trevi Fountain, where she would always throw a coin in the wishing fountain every time they visited Bernini's spectacular creation, seeing which Lena and Edwy would tease: 'Wishing for prince charming to come soon, aren't you?'

Gowramma was quite candid in her reply, 'Yes indeed, I want to visit Rome again with my handsome prince and children.'

The Carnival at Rome during the period of Lent was fast approaching, and as was the practice among the royalty and the nobles, the Logins too hired balconies on the main Corso, or the boulevard, in central Rome to witness the colourful parade. Princess Gowramma found herself among the important personalities of Europe; their neighbouring balcony was occupied by the members of the Prussian royal family. The eighteen-year-old prince of Wales (later King Edward VII) was also present in Rome for the winter along with his governor, General Bruce. During the Carnival, the young prince of Wales came over to the balcony occupied by Princess Gowramma and the Logins. To everyone's surprise, he presented a bouquet of flowers to the Indian princess. Gowramma blushed and fluttered her eyes in absolute delight. After spending a few minutes with them, he crossed over to meet his German cousins in the next balcony. The prince of Wales invited Gowramma and the Logins for dinner, where he had also asked Maharaja Duleep Singh and several other members of the European royal families.

Gowramma was in high spirits at the dinner hosted by the prince of Wales. She openly flirted with all the handsome young men, including the future king of England. The seductive look in her countenance, while talking to the dashing heir-apparent to the British throne, was not missed by the guests, including Maharaja Duleep Singh. The twenty-one-year-old maharaja had quite a few romantic flings with young women he had met with his rakish friend Samuel Baker. He now seriously wanted to find a life partner whom he could trust, and who would raise a family imbued with true Christian values.

He had dismissed the idea of marrying Gowramma earlier, but had come to Rome with a view to reconsider the proposal. He was acutely aware that an alliance between Princess Gowramma and him was very close to the heart of his sovereign, the queen. He had pondered on the issue; he and the princess got on well and were good friends, and they shared many common interests. However, Princess Gowramma's coquettish behaviour at various parties bothered Duleep Singh. He began to doubt if she would make a responsible wife and be serious about raising his children. He was a frequent visitor at 56, Capo la Casa, and spent long hours talking to the Logins. The Logins remained optimistic but to honour their earlier assurance to Duleep Singh, the topic of of the alliance with Gowramma was not discussed.

Duleep Singh, however, spoke at length about his wanting to settle down as early as possible and start a family. He seemed confused and anxious. His ongoing tussle with the East India Company and the government of India, regarding a hike in his allowance in accordance with the Lahore Treaty, had not been resolved in spite of Queen Victoria's intervention. On his attaining the age of eighteen, he was to get an annual pension of not les than four lakh rupees. Instead, the India Office hiked his allowance from 1,20,000 rupees to 2,50,000 rupees a year. They had also made it clear that Duleep Singh's children would not inherit the pension or properties after his demise.

Lady Login wrote a detailed account of the developments in Rome to Queen Victoria, which appeared to be turning out much better than expected. The frequent visits of Duleep Singh to their apartment made the Logins expect a proposal from the maharaja for Princess Gowramma to materialise any day.

The very next day, after Lady Login dispatched her report to the queen, there was another dinner party where Duleep Singh and princess Gowramma were guests. Lady Login was elated to see the maharaja having a quiet conversation with the princess, in a secluded corner. On their way home after the party, the Logins found the princess quiet and pensive. The following day maharaja Duleep Singh requested Lady Login for a private conversation. The Logins enthusiastically anticipated hearing a historic announcement from the maharaja; their expectations, built up over several years, seemed to be finally moving toward its desired conclusion. It would be a defining moment in the history of Britain and India. When Maharaja Duleep Singh arrived at 56, Capo la Casa, he was somber and seemed a little nervous. What he had to say, as described by Lady Login, was

bombshell exploded by the maharaja, shattering all the ideas and arrangements formed in the minds of the exalted personages interested in his future.'

Lady Login had to inform the queen immediately of the unexpected downturn. She wrote another detailed letter to Her Majesty on 31 March 1859:

Madam,

When I had the honour to address Your Majesty so lately, I did not anticipate the necessity of so soon again doing so, but as I am very greatly concerned at the purport of a conversation I have just had with the Maharaja, I am desirous of losing no time in making it known to Your Majesty.

The Maharajah met the Princess Gouramma a few evenings ago, at a small party, and I observed that he sat by her talking for some time. The next day he asked for a private interview with me, and, after saying that he thought the Princess much improved in manner and appearance, and that, he felt a sincere interest in her as his countrywoman. He said that he considered it only right and honourable on his part to tell me at once that he could not ask her to be his wife. That, from what he had observed of her lately, he had made up his mind that she was not calculated to make him happy, as he did not feel the confidence in her . . .he would in an English girl. I was much distressed at this, for I had hoped that she was conducting herself so as to make a favourable impression, . . . but he said repeatedly, 'I could never marry her! I could never feel more than pity for her! She would not be a safe wife for me! I don't seem to trust her! And I dread any trouble after marriage!'

He then went on to say that he felt very unhappy about himself, that he saw the necessity of altering many things in his own conduct and of endeavouring to live more as became his profession of Christianity, and his position in society. But that his temptations were so great, and he felt himself so weak to withstand them, that unless he could have some definite object in view, and some reward to strive after, he feared for the future . . . That up to this time his life had been aimless, that he felt he had no ties to bind him, no home or kindred that he could claim as his own, but that this could be altered if a hope could be held out to him that he might, at some future period, be permitted to try and win the love of one whom he had known and loved from her childhood, he would undergo any probation it was thought fit to impose on him, and strive, with God's help, to make himself worthy of her! . . . (Here he named a young relative of my husband, who had her in his care and charge) . . .

On observing the effect this utterly unexpected announcement had upon me, he became so confused and nervously excited, that he could not express his meaning clearly, and therefore begged I would give him no reply at present, but allow him to come next day and talk it over calmly.

I hope I need not assure Your Majesty that neither my husband, nor myself, had the slightest suspicion of the Maharajah's sentiments towards . . ., and that we were quite unprepared for his request, which caused us the greatest anxiety and pain on her account, even more than on the Maharajah's; and though we felt ourselves in a very peculiar position towards him, as his only Christian parents, and in a great degree bound to give him every aid we could, still, at the same time, this young girl's happiness and welfare must be paramount with us.

When he came the next morning, he said much of the great difficulty he should always find in becoming acquainted with the real disposition and character of any young lady he might meet in society; that in no other family could he be domesticated as he was with us; that he had known ---'s temper and disposition thoroughly, and watched her closely, and had long felt that . . . she was in every respect what he wished for in his wife;

her truthfulness and purity he could rely on, and her religious feelings he reverenced. But if we, whom he trusted and regarded as parents, could not accept him into the family; if we, who had taken him from his own country and people, and cut him off (though at his own request) from all prospect of mixing with his own race, should refuse to regard him as one of ourselves, to whom could he look? I earnestly hope that in the reply that we have given, we have been rightly directed, and that, with God's blessing, the event may result in good. We have told the Maharajah that in our peculiar situation, and as Christians, we cannot altogether refuse his request, though we must adopt such measures as shall, as far as possible, render our present concession harmless to the other person involved, . . . as she must be our first consideration; that in the earnest hope that this may lead him to higher views of the duties of his position, and of his Christian profession. If it was found that for the next three years his conduct gave us confidence in his sincerity, and in the depth of his present feelings, and in the event of his obtaining Your Majesty's gracious approval, we would allow him to plead his own cause with the young girl, who would then be of age sufficient to make the decision for herself. In the meantime, he bound himself, on his honour, not in any way to make her aware of his sentiments. We, on our part, being careful that they shall see as little as possible of each other in the interim.

We have told him that we make this promise, and hold out this inducement to him, solely in the hope that, before this period expires, he will see his true position more clearly, and meet with someone more suitable in every respect, . . . as we in no wise covet such a destiny for our charge. . . . We felt that to deprive him of all hope, considering the position we have held towards him, would have been both un-Christian and injudicious, and might have led him to become utterly careless. There were many circumstances which I cannot detail by letter, which have strengthened us in resolving on this reply. My first impulse was to return straight to England, instead of going on to Naples, in the hope of being permitted personally to lay everything before Your Majesty. On second thoughts, knowing how much Your Majesty desired that the Princess should be as long abroad as possible, and that her health would be benefited by a stay at the seaside, I have decided to adhere to our first intention. Need I express to Your Majesty with what deep anxiety I shall await at Naples the expression of Your Majesty's opinion on the course we have thought it our duty to pursue with respect to the Maharajah?

I have the honour to be, Madam, with most dutiful and grateful respects, Your Majesty's most humble and most devoted servant,

Lena Login

The Logins found themselves in quite a predicament regarding their future plans and arrangements. Lady Login was also upset that it was the behaviour of Princess Gowramma, which had put off the maharaja. In her frustration, she berated the princess for the undesirable impression she had made on Maharaja Duleep Singh because of her conduct. 'All the efforts of Mrs Drummond, Dr Login, and mine to make you an ideal Christian princess seems to have come to naught,' she lamented.

Princess Gowramma took the criticism quite stoically. The entire episode, however, had a sobering effect on Gowramma.

In the days that followed, there was a marked improvement in Gowramma's conduct, but it was too late. The Logins were more disappointed than Gowramma that Maharaja Duleep Singh had rejected the alliance. What could have been a crowning achievement, was shattered forever. To further complicate matters for the Logins, Duleep Singh had fallen madly in love with a niece of Sir Login, who was a minor.

Lady Login wrote to Queen Victoria to find out whether she should explore possibilities of an alliance for the Coorg princess with some of the eligible bachelors from the Prussian Court who were residing in Rome at the time to attend on the ailing King Frederick William IV. They also started making plans to return to England. By the middle of April, they moved from Rome to Naples, and after spending a few days there, travelled south to Sorrento. Sir Charles Phipps replied on behalf of the queen.

My dear Lady Login,

The Queen has received and read with great interest your letters of the 26th and 31st March.

Her Majesty fully comprehends, and sympathizes with, the conflicting feelings with which you must have received the unexpected declaration of the Maharajah, and Her Majesty thinks that, considering all the circumstances, the decision at which you arrived was not only the soundest and most prudent, but also the kindest and the most likely to be beneficial towards the Maharajah.

... If his attachment to this young lady is deeply-rooted and really sincere, it may afford him a sufficient object to strengthen and render permanent his good resolutions, and thus establish a strong motive for good, so much wanting in an indolent and self indulgent, though generous, honourable and upright nature, such as his. The Queen has, therefore, no doubt that you answered him both wisely, and in accordance with that affectionate regard which you and Sir John have ever shown him. . . .

Her Majesty hopes that the conversation which you have had with the Princess . . . may have a good effect, and that a marriage with some other eligible person may be effected. It would be desirable that any such prospect, with a person whom you would approve, should be in every way encouraged. It is most probable that union with a sensible and kind husband, whom she could respect and look up to, might have the most desirable effect upon her character. The Queen entirely approves of your decision not to return home immediately, and is quite of opinion that a little longer stay abroad is likely to be, in every way, the best plan for her.

With regard to her [Gowramma's] presentation at Court, the Queen thinks that whenever it shall be decided that she is to come out in London, it will not be necessary for her to be presented at Court at all. Having been for many years under Her Majesty's protection, such a ceremony would not be required; but the Queen thinks that the decision as to her coming out at all this year, must depend very much upon the report which you are able to make upon your return to England. It does not, at present, seem improbable, that it may be thought prudent to delay for another year her general introduction into Society. As, from her rank, and the peculiarities of her position, she will be very much watched . . . anything unusual in her manner would be made subject of general remark, and might have a most prejudicial effect upon her prospects, which must, for her happiness and future welfare, be directed to secure a suitable marriage.

It gives me great pleasure to be able thus to convey to you the entire approbation of the Queen of the course you have pursued, under circumstances of certainly unusual difficulty.

C.B. Phipps

Queen Victoria's interest in her goddaughter showed the first signs of waning. She wanted the Logins to keep Princess Gowramma abroad a little longer. The government of India, now directly under the British government, reneging on honouring the Lahore Treaty, bothered the queen. She was unable to influence the India Office who kept stalling the entire issue. The monarchy in the United Kingdom had undergone several changes with the House of Commons becoming the centre of power. The monarchy had only 'the right to be consulted, the right to advice, and the right to warn.'

Lady Login wrote back to Sir Phipps on 25 April 1859, informing the palace that they would return to London with Princess Gowramma in about a fortnight, and would take the first opportunity to meet Her Majesty to explain all that had transpired in Rome. Lady Login opined that the introduction of the princess to society should not be delayed by another year, as suggested by Her Majesty. She expressed her apprehensions to Sir Phipps that the presence of Veerarajendra in England would be a great obstacle to his daughter making a good marriage. She hoped that the raja's affairs might be arranged without further delay by the Indian Council to facilitate his speedy return to India.

The time spent in Rome was the happiest and the most memorable for Princess Gowramma. The rejection by Maharaj

Duleep Singh and the subsequent coldness in the attitude of the Logins had begun to cast its shadow on her. She however, tried her best to maintain a cheerful demeanour. The schedule was more relaxed at Naples and Sorrento. Three months in the warmer weather, the sunshine and proximity to the sea had improved her health. Gowramma felt better and more energetic, but she was deeply concerned about the future. Since she had plenty of time on her hands, the Logins insisted the princess read books along with their children, Lena and Edwy. Lady Login helped Princess Gowramma write a long letter detailing the historical places visited in Rome, to Princess Alice who was closest to Gowramma among the nine children of the queen. The letter was dispatched in the diplomatic bag to the Buckingham Palace. The thought of soon returning to the wet English weather and uncertainly about her future dampened Gowramma's spirits.

As any other woman, Princess Gowramma wanted to have children and a home of her own. Deep inside, she was not entirely unhappy that the alliance with Duleep Singh had failed. Gowramma felt European and she was keen to have an English husband. She wanted no involvement with anything associated with her land of birth. She dreaded the thought of ever going back to Benares or any other part of India. She would often pray, holding the cross to her lips: 'Jesus Christ, I wish to live in Rome forever with my husband and children. I beseech you my Lord, please make it happen.'

Gowramma did everything possible to please the Logins and make amends for her indiscretions. She now sadly realised that the royal balls and parties, the many glasses of wine, the dancing and flirting with good-looking men, who were only too happy to bestow attention on her, had gone to her head. Her large dark brown eyes and exotic looks, which elicited the attention of men, had excited her. She dreamt of true love and happiness, and was fascinated with men with blue eyes; but to her disappointment, none went on their knees to propose to her! Gowramma was dismayed that one of the reasons coming in the way of eligible suitors proposing to her was her father, whom the British society continued to view as an 'old reprobate'.

The Logins settled down to a quiet stay in Naples. Princess Gowramma missed the parties, and the leisurely walks and sight-seeing trips of Rome. The days spent in the warm weather in Rome had considerably improved her health. She realised that the only family she could now call her own was that of the Logins. To her disappointment, the Logins were also not as warm as they used to be to her. Gowramma was aware that the queen too was unhappy with her and she now dreaded the thought of being made to live with some other family, or worse, being sent back to Benares.

9

IN LOVE WITH GEORGE CHRISTMAS

$\mathcal{B}$Y THE MIDDLE of May, 1859, the Logins and Princess Gowramma were back in London after their three months' eventful trip through Europe. The Logins were happy to be back at Kew, and looked forward to a normal family life. They celebrated the first birthday of their youngest child Mabel, though it was held after the event. Lady Lena Login was also keen to be relieved of her responsibilities of chaperoning Princess Gowramma. Maharaja Duleep Singh had returned from his wanderings in Europe, and he frequently requested Lady Login to play hostess his homes at Mulgrave Castle and Auchlyne in Perthshire. He always insisted on Lady Login bringing her children along. After the recent developments, dealing with both Princess Gowramma

...aharaja Duleep Singh had become embarrassing for Lady ...ogin. She also wanted to devote more time to her six children. Her requests were finally acknowledged and she was informed by the palace that Lady Catherine Harcourt had agreed to take charge of the Indian princess. Lady Login was summoned by the queen for an audience; for Princess Gowramma, her worst fears had come true.

Lady Login narrated to the queen the details of their sojourn in the Continent. The queen instructed Lady Login to take Princess Gowramma for a forthcoming State Concert, where she could be introduced to her new guardian, Lady Catherine Harcourt, wife of Colonel Vernon Harcourt. The queen also instructed that the princess should make her appearance at a State Ball on 8 June 1859, under the joint chaperonage of Lady Login and Lady Harcourt. The State Ball, which had about 1900 invitees, included Maharaja Duleep Singh as well. It was a splendid affair with the quadrille band of Coote & Tinney performing a selection of dance music from the works of Strauss, D'Albert, Gung'l and the Hon C.H. Lindsay.

To Princess Gowramma's relief and delight, she was invited by Her Majesty for a drawing room get-together at St. James' Place on 11 June 1859, under the sole charge of Lady Catherine. However, Lady Catherine was unable to attend, and the responsibility once again fell on Lady Login, who had to escort Princess Gowramma on her debut in the royal circle. Princess Gowramma basked in all the attention she received. The queen was hopeful that with these high profile exposures to the British upper class, her goddaughter would soon find a suitor. Princess Gowramma's transfer to the care of Lady Catherine was finally fixed for 23 June 1859.

By then Veerarajendra, whose health was failing, had taken seriously ill. The fifty-seven-year-old raja was crestfallen that his case against the East India Company was faltering and seemed doomed to failure. The Company had contended that the two deposits in question were not the private property of the raja; hence, it belonged to the state. His lawyers too did not sound confident any longer.

Even though he had come to England with permission to stay for a year, it was seven years since Veerarajendra had left Benares. As far as his daughter was concerned, he was more than happy that Princess Gowramma was being well cared for by Her Majesty. He had fulfilled the dying wish of Devammaji in ensuring a good life for Gowramma, though he had doubts if his late wife would have approved of her daughter renouncing the Hindu faith. It was his dream now to see Gowramma married to an English nobleman, and he hoped his daughter would soon find a rich and influential husband. Nevertheless, the news of the alliance with Maharaja Duleep Singh having failed, had disappointed him.

With his hopes of winning the case diminishing with each passing day, Veerarajendra was now depressed. Troubled by ill health, he reflected a great deal about his wives and children in India. Gowramma had briefly met him on her return from Rome. He very much wanted her to spend a few days with him, but she did not show much interest, and the Logins too discouraged her. To make matters worse, Veerarajendra found that his daughter could no longer speak her mother tongue. Mudduveeramma too was frustrated that she could not converse with Gowramma. She tried to convince her stepdaughter to stay and comfort her sick father. Within a few days of this meeting, Veerarajendra's health suddenly took a turn for the worse and he was bed-ridden. He sent word for his daughter to stay close by and visit him as often as possible.

At that time, Lady Catherine Harcourt was living in the Isle of Wight. Because of Veerarajendra's poor health, Gowramma's shift to the Harcourts' had to be postponed. It was decided that she would stay in Kew with the Logins for a while. Gowramma visited her father at Clifton Villas a few times along with Lady Login, who now had to perform the additional duty of an interpreter between father and daughter! Lady Login had to translate Gowramma's English into Hindustani for the raja. Aware that her father's presence in London was a major impediment in prospective suitors proposing to her, Princess Gowramma wished him to return to Benares. In Lady Login's words: 'I took the daughter over from Kew once or twice to see the poor old man, but it was a very painful business. He was really fond of her, but she seemed to be quite indifferent, and showed very little feeling.'

However, Veerarajendra's condition improved considerably during the next fortnight and it was decided that Princess Gowramma could join the Harcourts at the Isle of Wight. Gowramma was not too happy; she did not relish moving in with the elderly Harcourts.

Lady Login accompanied Princess Gowramma to see her father before her departure to the Isle of Wight. Veerarajendra's face lit up on seeing his favourite daughter. Walking with great difficulty, he unlocked a cupboard and asked Gowramma to help him take out the rosewood box, which he had zealously guarded since their departure from Benares. He then took out a crimson satin bag full of jewels and said to his daughter:

'These jewels, gems, and gold coins are my gift to you, my dearest kombakki. Some of the jewellery in the bag belonged to your dear mother. I wanted to present these to you on your wedding day.' Tired with the effort of speaking, he paused for a while and continued, 'Now I am not sure if I will be alive to see that wonderful event. I am so happy I could witness your baptism and confirmation. May God bless you. May Her Majesty, the queen, continue to look after you. When I get better, I would like to return to Benares. I have given up hopes of getting the funds due to me from the rapacious Company.'

Saying this, the raja lay down on his bed, drained of all energy. Gowramma left her father's room tightly clutching the red satin bag.

The jewellery, gold and precious gems that Veerarajendra gave Gowramma were worth a fortune. She fantasised wearing these ornaments for the grand functions in London, but she had no control over her future. It was a painful experience for the Logins to see a highly reluctant and tearful Princess Gowramma take leave of them to join her new guardian. Gowramma also resented the fact that Lady Harcourt had decided to put her under the supervision of a governess, Miss Sharp, who had come to escort her to the Isle of Wight.

In the meantime, Veerarajendra made a formal request to the queen. Worried that his end was near, he wanted Her Majesty to permit him to bring his seven sons to London so that they too could get the benefit of European education. He said he wished to make amends to his sons. The queen referred this to the Governor-General Lord Canning. The government of India, however, recognised only one of the sons of the raja as a 'legitimate' heir. Under pressure from the queen, Sir Charles Wood of the

India Office wrote an official letter to the governor-general on 30 June 1859. There was some progress in the request to allow the 'legitimate' son, Lingarajendra, to come to England. Veerarajendra, by then almost bedridden, eagerly awaited confirmation from the governor-general. However, the government of India, in keeping with their deliberate strategy, delayed the process. It was felt that London already had a surfeit of Indian royalties and the India Office wanted to discourage this influx.

A few days after Princess Gowramma was escorted by Miss Sharp to the Isle of Wight, Lady Login received a message from the queen. The letter, a hand-written note from Her Majesty (Victoria Regina), was very special to Lady Login:

My Dear Lady Login,

Princess Gouramma having now finally been given over to Lady Catherine Harcourt, I wish to express to you my sense of the great improvement which I find in her since she has been under your charge, and I thank you for all the kind and affectionate care you took of her, and the trouble you gave yourself in watching over this interesting child. May she turn out as we could wish!

With the Prince's kind remembrance and ours to Sir John Login, believe me,

Yours sincerely,
'Victoria R'

The letter was sealed with the queen's private coat-of-arms. Lady Login was overwhelmed at Her Majesty's gesture, and all the trouble and anxiety she had to experience over Princess Gowramma seemed worthwhile. There was more appreciation from the queen; a jeweller's packet arrived a week later from Osborne. Sir Charles Phipps wrote on behalf of the queen:

Dear Lady Login,

I am very glad that you were so much pleased with the Queen's letter.

I have now received Her Majesty's commands to forward to you the accompanying bracelet, as a more durable mark of her appreciation of the readiness with which you undertook a charge, at a time when it was inconvenient to yourself, and of the admirable manner in which you discharged the duties, which thereby devolved upon you.

With kindest remembrances to Sir John,

Ever sincerely yours,
C.B. Phipps

The bracelet, a plain gold gipsy band, was set with three fine stones—an emerald, diamond and ruby, with the words 'To Lady Login, V.R., 1859' engraved inside.

A very unhappy Princess Gowramma left the Logins from Church House in Kew in July 1859. Having earlier lived in Ryde with the Drummonds, she was not too fond of the island. To make matters worse, the Harcourts were strict disciplinarians and devout Christians. They set a rigid schedule for the princess with very little time for socialising.

Aged eighteen years, the princess resented being treated as an immature young girl. It was only when the queen visited Osborne that she received invitations for functions with the royal family. During this dismal period in her life, the only memorable event princess Gowramma attended was at Osborne House. Chaperoned by Colonel and Lady Catherine Harcourt, Gowramma was a guest at the fifteenth birthday of Prince Alfred on 6 August 1859. The event cheered Gowramma immensely, and she was reassured that Her Majesty still cared for her. The princess was again invited by the queen a few days later to witness the regatta organised by the seamen and marines of the Royal yachts at East Cowes near Osborne. After the departure of the royal family from Osborne, it was back to a drab life with the Harcourts.

By September 1859, Veerarajendra's health started to deteriorate further. His liver and lungs were failing alarmingly. The helplessness and hopelessness that he experienced in Benares came to haunt him again. All the hope and expectations he had entertained in fair play by the British had evaporated. He saw a similar fate descending on Maharaja Duleep Singh and the prince of Oudh.

During the past two years, there had been no invitations for the raja of Coorg, from the queen or the India Office for any of the functions. To add to Veerarajendra's woes, his daughter's indifference broke his heart. The situation at Clifton Villas was depressing. Mudduveeramma and Siddaveeramma were miserable and terribly homesick, but the two women and the servants attended on the raja diligently. Veerarajendra wanted to reward them for their loyalty. He summoned his solicitors and dictated his will, wherein he named Sir John Login and a confidant named Robert Montgomery Martin as the executors of his will.

With every passing day, Veerarajendra's condition worsened. His troubled mind started to hallucinate, and in his delirious state, his thoughts were transported to the painful last days in his kingdom. The tune of the 'British Grenadier' that he had detested ever since he was dethroned, reverberated relentlessly deep in his head. He was agitated and kept muttering, 'Stop th band. Stop the band.' His wife Mudduveeramma and the servants could not understand what the raja wanted. He could not get the sound of the band out of his brain. By 24 September 1859, he was too feeble, and could only whisper 'stop the band.' The doctor attending on him warned his household that the raja was unlikely to survive the day. His last request, as life ebbed out of his body, was for sacred water from the Ganges.

Veerarajendra's demise was conveyed to his solicitors, who in turn informed Robert Montgomery Martin and Sir John Login. Both the gentlemen were surprised that the raja had nominated them to be executors of his will. The raja had also appointed Sir Login to represent him in pursuing the case against the East India Company. Sir Login was away at Scotland at the time, and Montgomery Martin being close by, was the first to visit 20, Clifton Villas, and make enquiries. The solicitors informed him that a considerable amount of the raja's jewels, valuables and artifacts had disappeared from the residence as the raja lay dying. Montgomery Martin had to immediately secure the large quantity of treasure still lying in the house including the contents in the rosewood jewellery box. He instructed the solicitors to make a list of the jewels, precious gems, ornaments, ivory, rare artifacts and substantial quantities of gold and silver coins. He arranged for the well-known jewellers, Ryder and Hancock, to evaluate the assets of the raja, which were finally estimated at 17,319 pound sterling. The jewels and other valuables were placed in sealed containers and deposited in a safevault in Westminster Bank at Lothbury. The Harcourts arranged for Gowramma to travel to London to attend the last rites of her father.

During Veerarajendra's stay in London, he had befriended Rev W. McArthur, the Secretary to the Wesleyan Mission in

London. The priest had worked in India for many years at the Mysore branch of the mission. Rev McArthur was conversant with Kannada, Veerarajendra's mother tongue. He was one of the few in London with whom the raja could have a conversation, and they had met frequently. He helped Veerarajendra in maintaining communication with his family in Benares. Between Montgomery Martin and Rev McArthur, it was decided to temporarily intern the body of the raja in an unconsecrated catacomb at Kensal Green Cemetery. Veerarajendra's mortal remains were placed in a lead and oak coffin. Before the deceased was taken out of 20, Clifton Villas, Rev McArthur performed the funeral rites according to the practices of the Church of England, even though Veerarajendra was a Hindu. There was shock and outrage at the action, by the conservatives in London. However, there were many at the service who appreciated the solemn prayers offered for the soul of the deceased. Rev McArthur stated that in the time that he had known the raja, he had heard highly favourable opinions from him about Christianity. He further justified his actions saying that the raja had guided his favourite daughter Princess Victoria Gowramma to take the path shown by Jesus Christ. He also informed the congregation that the message of Jesus Christ was being propagated in the raja's erstwhile kingdom. Rev Herman Moegling, the German protestant priest, had set up a Protestant Mission in Coorg, which was making progress, though the programme had fallen short of expectations.

The raja's secretary, John James Birkett, communicated the news of Veerarajendra's demise to his family in Benares. By the time the message reached India and the contents were explained to his wives at Coorg Nest, it was October 1859. On hearing the news, two of his devoted wives performed sati, a predominantly north Indian practice, by consuming an overdose of opium in order to 'join' their husband in afterlife. Two more wives made half-hearted attempts to end their lives by starving to death, but were apprehended and taken to the state-run hospital. They willingly allowed themselves to be 'forced' to take food.

Mudduveeramma, Siddaveeramma and the servants who looked after the raja in London returned to Benares after a long and tedious journey. They were relieved to be back with their own people at last. To their dismay, the other widows of Veerarajendra raised objection to their entering Coorg Nest. It was insisted that those who accompanied the raja and crossed the seas undertake a purification bath in the Ganges and perform poojas. After Mudduveeramma and Siddaveeramma carried out these rituals, they were allowed to enter Coorg Nest. All the surviving wives of Veerarajendra wore white clothes and were bereft of ornaments. Mudduveeramma and Siddaveeramma spent the next few days narrating incredible stories of their experience in faraway London. Subadhramma was sad to hear that her foster daughter Gowramma had changed inexorably. It pained her to hear that Gowramma had forgotten Kannada, and still worse, had turned indifferent towards her father. Subadhramma had agonised over a similar situation with her own daughter Gangamma, who too had lost touch with her mother tongue, and could only communicate with difficulty with her and other relatives. Gangamma, however, continued to be in touch with her family and visited Benares at regular intervals after her marriage to Jung Bahadur. It was apparent to all in Coorg Nest that it was highly unlikely that Gowramma would ever return to Benares.

Robert Montgomery Martin wrote to the Secretary of State for India, informing him of the steps taken by him as the executor of the raja's will. He made an appeal to the India Office to instruct the British Resident at Benares to secure and assess the raja's assets there, so that his wealth could be distributed among his sons, daughters, wives, other relatives and servants as willed by the raja in his testament.

On receiving instructions from Sir Charles Wood of the India Office, the Resident at Benares deputed a civilian named F.B. Gubbins to Coorg Nest to take possession of all the jewels and other treasures of Veerarajendra. However, Gubbins found that just like what had happened at 20, Clifton Villas, London, all the valuable possessions of the raja had disappeared! On repeated questioning and pressure on the family, it was revealed that some of the sons of the raja had surreptitiously buried the valuables within the large compound of Coorg Nest. The buried assets were unearthed and secured by Gubbins. All the jewellery, gems, coins and artifacts were listed and placed in sealed containers. Veerarajendra's wealth at Benares was valued at 17,822 pound sterling. These were kept in the portico of the haveli with an armed guard, until the apportioning of the property could be taken up as detailed in the will. F.B. Gubbins came under a great deal of criticism for his flippant and insensitive treatment of the members of a royal family. Gubbins had nearly lost his life during the uprising in 1857 and ever since was extremely harsh on Indians.

Back in London, the Harcourts had shifted from Ryde to their estate at Buxted Park in Sussex. Princess Gowramma was lonely and found living with the strict, fussy and elderly Harcourts unbearably dull. She became sullen and obstinate. It was during this depressed state of mind that Gowramma befriended George Christmas, the under-butler in the household.

George Christmas was a blue-eyed lad, who was the only one in the household who made the otherwise sullen princess laugh at his witty conversation. The lonely princess found relief from the dreary days in the company of the gregarious George Christmas, and soon the princess madly fell in love with the boy. She and George had several furtive trysts. Then one day, in the middle of the night the Harcourts heard sounds of movement in the house. Colonel Harcourt came armed with a gun to confront the intruder, only to find the princess in a dressing gown thrown over her petticoat sans the stays! She was tiptoeing with her footwear in hand. Lady Harcourt too came on the scene and Gowramma was confronted with a barrage of questions. Gowramma shedding torrential tears blurted, 'I am very unhappy here. I want to run away. I am on my way to the station.' She was pacified and asked to return to her room.

However, the next morning a letter written by the princess to the under-butler was discovered and her true intentions came to light. She had also sent a volume of Longfellow's poems to her paramour. The lovesick princess had earlier confided in her maid, 'If they send me anywhere else, and prevent me from marrying George, I will take my own life.' In one of her missives, Gowramma quoted a poem by Shelley:

To suffer woes which Hope thinks infinite;
To forgive wrongs darker than Death or Night;
To defy Power which seems Omnipotent;
To love, and bear; to hope, till Hope creates
From its own wreck the thing it contemplates. . .

The Harcourts, steeped in Victorian ideals on morality and family values, were outraged and shocked beyond reconciliation.

They wanted to be immediately relieved of their responsibilities of looking after the princess. Lady Harcourt wrote to Lady Lena Login, expressing her exasperation in managing the intractable princess. Lady Login, having looked after Gowramma, was more understanding. In her *Recollections*, Lady Login expressed her feelings in these words:

> I could not but feel sorry for Lady Catherine, a most conscientious, kind-hearted woman, but could scarcely refrain from smiling at her expression of horrified reprobation of this young girl, in the letters she wrote to me at the time, though I could quite imagine that the culprit's air of stolid indifference would make her appear utterly 'callous', and perverse. But my sympathy went out even more to the ignorant child, rigorously punished for faults due to early up-bringing in an Indian zenana, and not wisely corrected when first brought under the influence of Christian morality. There was something so exceedingly attractive, and amiable, in her natural manner, that I for one regarded her with a very sincere affection, and this I believe she genuinely reciprocated.

Surprisingly, when Queen Victoria heard the details of the scandalous behaviour of her troubled goddaughter princess Gowramma, she was quite understanding. She recommended another trip to the Continent to calm the nerves of the Princess, and to avoid the growing scurrilous gossip. Prince Albert too was of the view that 'the feeling of inferiority to European civilised society may have depressed and made her desperate.'

Lady Harcourt was not prepared to continue with her charge fearing the princess could harm herself in her disturbed state of mind. Under instructions from the queen, the Lord Chancellor arranged for Princess Gowramma to move closer to London. She was put under the guardianship of her godfather, Sir James Weir-Hogg. By mid-1860, Gowramma and her governess, Miss Sharp, had moved in with the Weir-Hoggs. Princess Gowramma, though happy to be in London, was heart-broken at the separation from her lover. Her new guardians reminded her that it was disgraceful for a goddaughter of the queen to be mixed up with an under-butler. Her earlier brush with the stable-boy while with the Drummonds had already tarnished her reputation. They impressed it upon her to behave like a princess, failing which, they warned her that no respectable suitor would want an alliance with her.

But what Gowramma could not tell the Weir-Hoggs was that she was weary of waiting for a suitor from British high society.

10

DULEEP SINGH PLAYS MATCHMAKER

DURING THE YEAR 1860, Maharaja Duleep Singh was dividing his time between his leased lodge in Auchlyne, and Mulgrave Castle in Yorkshire. By then Colonel Oliphant, the former Chairman of the Court of Directors of the East India Company, had taken over from Sir Login the charge of handling the maharaja's affairs on Queen Victoria's suggestion. The Colonel, who had incurred heavy financial losses, was happy to receive from Duleep Singh a salary of 800 pound sterling a year. Duleep Singh hoped that Colonel Oliphant would help him in his efforts to reclaim the allowances owed to him by the India Office. The maharaja, however, voluntarily continued to pay 1000 pound sterling annually to his mentors, Sir John Login and Lady Login.

Duleep Singh was sympathetic when he heard the news about Princess Gowramma; he could well understand the inner conflicts she was facing. At Mulgrave and Auchlyne, he frequently entertained large number of guests from the British upper classes, where Lady Login would help and play hostess. Duleep Singh began to invite Gowramma to his parties so that she could meet some of the eligible bachelors. Around this time, Lady Login's brother, Lt. Colonel John Campbell, returned to England, having retired from military service with the 38th Madras Native Infantry in India. He had lost his wife a few years earlier, and was father of a large brood of children. The nearly fifty-year-old Colonel was blue-eyed, handsome and possessed a dashing personality. A keen equestrian, he was also fond of hunting and outdoor activities and soon became well acquainted with Duleep Singh. Gradually, the Colonel became a frequent visitor, joining the maharaja in grouse shooting, along with several well-known members from the British royalty, which on occasions, included the prince of Wales.

It was at Mulgrave Castle that Maharaja Duleep Singh decided to arrange a meeting between the nineteen-year-old Princess Gowramma and his debonair friend Colonel Campbell. The charming and witty Colonel swept the gullible princess off her feet. The wily Colonel was also attracted to the fabulous jewellery owned by the Coorg princess and her 400-pound sterling allowance. There was also the possibility of Veerarajendra's suit against East India Company yielding huge benefits. Their romance progressed without Lady Login getting wind of it. Sir Weir-Hogg had also relaxed the restrictions on the Indian princess to encourage her to make new friends. Duleep Singh, who was feeling quite satisfied with his matchmaking efforts, was however taken aback when suddenly one fine day Gowramma and Colonel Campbell came to inform him that they had decided to tie the knot.

Lady Login was thunderstruck when she heard from Sir Charles Phipps the news of Princess Gowramma's engagement to her brother. She was even more surprised when informed that the queen too had given her consent, as Her Majesty was confident that a brother of Lady Login would certainly be an honourable gentleman. The queen was happy that her difficult goddaughter was at last on the verge of settling down and 'a quiet and comfortable, though not brilliant home was secured for her.' Sir Weir-Hogg was also pleased that the princess was finally settling down with someone she loved and admired. The Logins, on the other hand, were not too happy at the nineteen-year-old princess marrying someone thirty years her senior. Lady Login was annoyed with her brother who was older than her by a few years!

On 17 July 1860, Colonel John Campbell and Princess Victoria Gowramma solemnised their marriage in a simple ceremony at St George's Church near Hanover Square. The blissful contentment that Princess Gowramma displayed after her marriage finally reconciled Lady Login to the fact that her young ward was now her sister-in-law! Princess Gowramma was thrilled to be a member of Lady Login's family and she promptly started referring to Lady Lena Login as 'sister'. Gowramma was delighted that she was now an aunt to the Login children. The first visit of the newlyweds was to meet and thank their matchmaker Maharaja Duleep Singh who insisted he be the godfather to their firstborn.

Soon after their marriage, Colonel Campbell took his young bride to Kinloch in Scotland, his place of birth, to spend a few months at the estate of his elder brother, General Charles Campbell. After years of vicissitudes, Princess Gowramma wa finally happy at the opportunity to enjoy domestic bliss. She made an affectionate and devoted wife to Colonel Campbell, and was genuinely fond of his family.

Sir Login continued to pursue Veerarajendra's suit against the East India Company. The final verdict on the case was announced on 8 December 1860, at Rolls' Court in Chancery Lane, where Sir John Login was present as the legal representative of the late raja of Coorg. The Master of the Rolls in his statement gave a detailed preamble of the suit before pronouncing his judgment:

...The principal difficulty I have felt in this case has arisen from the double character filled by the defendants, the East India Company. They were both a company of merchants trading in East Indies and also a foreign Power; and, as far as the Rajah of Coorg is concerned, an independent Sovereign State at war with him. Hence it follows that the acts done by the defendants are frequently ambiguous, and it becomes extremely difficult to ascertain whether any particular act is to be attributed to the exercise of their political power as a Sovereign State, or to be taken as the acts of a company of merchants trading to the East Indies. If this case can fairly be represented to be the instance of a foreign Power taking an enemy prisoner, and by means thereof obtaining possession of documents which established his rights to recover a debt due from another to him in his private capacity, then I am clear that the plaintiff is entitled to relief, and the circumstance of the defendants being both the conquering Power and the debtors does not vary the question. But, if the [promissory] notes were the property of the plaintiff in his character of Rajah, and if they were taken possession of by the defendants in the exercise of their sovereign and political power, then I am equally clear that this Court cannot interfere. On the first point, the evidence satisfies me that the [promissory] notes belonged to the plaintiff in his character as Rajah of Coorg, and not in any private character apart from such office. It is clear that unless he had been Rajah of Coorg he could not have had any rights to them, or any means of obtaining possession of them, nor could have procured the payment of interest or dividends due upon them. It was for the plaintiff to establish that the [promissory] notes were his property in his private right, and that under the law regulating inheritance in Coorg he could have been possessed of them if he had not been Rajah. But the plaintiff has not complied with this obligation, the evidence, as far as it goes, tending to show that the plaintiff would not have been entitled to the notes but for his character of Rajah. If so, they were held by him as part of the *jura regalia,* and not as private property. They were both taken possession of by the defendants; one by their superintendent and commissioned political officer of the Government, and the other under an indemnity given to the agent of the plaintiff in the manner to which I have already adverted. These circumstances amount, in my opinion, to taking possession of the notes on the part of the defendants in the exercise of their sovereign and political power. It is clear that in this mode of taking the notes it was in no mercantile character that they took and retained them. If this be so—as in my opinion it is—then the authorities upon which the plaintiff relies, and the answer of the Duke of Newcastle to the Prussian Government on the seizure of Silesian debt due to British subjects, upon which so much stress has been laid, do not apply. The case, in my opinion, falls within the rule laid down and the cases cited in the case of 'The East India

Company v. the Rajah of Tanjore.' I am of the opinion that the taking possession of the notes by the East India Government were acts done in the exercise of their sovereign power, and that those acts are not subject to the control of this Court. I must therefore direct the bill to be dismissed, but I shall do so, under the circumstances of the case, without cost.

Princess Gowramma was deeply disappointed at the verdict. She lamented over the anguish her father had undergone during his lifetime over the case. However, she was not too upset for life had opened a new door to her; she had discovered that she was expecting her first child.

When Sir Login communicated the news of the dismissal of the suit to the family of Veerarajendra in Benares, gloom and despair descended on the raja's household. The family, though aware of the situation, had entertained the hope that Sir Login would somehow help them win the case. The raja's sons now pleaded with Sir Login to get them at least the pension Veerarajendra was drawing until his demise. The Indian government had stopped the allowance, pending instructions from the India Office in London.

Veerarajendra's mortal remains lay in the catacomb in Kensal Green Cemetery until early 1861. Sir John Login used his influence with the India Office to arrange for the body of Veerarajendra to be sent by ship SS Lady Milville to Calcutta, and from there by horse carriage to Benares. The raja's family performed the last rites at the jangamvadi, the Lingayat religious mutt in Benares. The embalmed body of the raja was buried within the compound of the jangamvadi and a memorial was built over it. The British government spent an amount of 2,500 rupees for these rites, and the construction of the monument, which was completed in April 1861.

The India Office and the governor-general took over two years before deciding on the pension for the raja's family. Veerarajendra's children, wives and close relations numbered about twenty individuals. After repeated reminders from Sir Login to the India Office, Lord Canning approved a monthly pension of 3,000 rupees. Under instructions from the queen, Princess Victoria Gowramma was settled with a yearly allowance of 1000 pound sterling for life.

With the allowance for Gowramma now more than doubled, Colonel Campbell moved his wife to 27, Porchester Terrace in London. Gowramma's health, never robust, caused several complications and she had a difficult pregnancy. She was in great discomfort and looked to her husband for support. But to her dismay, Colonel Campbell grew more and more aloof with each passing day. His attitude towards her had changed ever since the dismissal of Veerarajendra's case against the East India Company.

In her hour of need, Princess Gowramma turned to Lady Login for support. Despite all the problems, she desperately looked forward to the birth of her child and a family of her own, and she weathered her difficulties with fortitude. On 2 July 1861, she gave birth to a baby girl. The baby was christened Edith Victoria Gowramma Campbell. One of the early visitor at Porchester Terrace to see the mother and child was Maharaj Duleep Singh, who presented the infant a silver cup and a spoon. Princess Gowramma was pleased and greatly reassured when the maharaja promised to be godfather to little Edith.

Gowramma found immense solace in bringing up her daughter. Edith was a healthy bonny baby, and Gowramma only disappointment was that her daughter had not inherited th colonel's blue eyes. As Edith grew, her pranks kept Gowramma in splits of laughter. Colonel Campbell was by now an indifferent husband. With the allowance she received from the India Office, Gowramma maintained a good home and provided all the necessities for Edith.

In her lonely moments, she would remember her father and her family in Benares. She received occasional news from visitors from India about her half-sister Gangamma, now Jung Bahadur's wife. Gangamma, who had been strikingly beautiful as a young girl, had grown to be a very elegant woman. A doctor named Dr Ambrose Oldfield, who served as the resident doctor in the court of Jung Bahadur, wrote of an incident concerning Princess Gangamma in his book about the powerful prime minister of Nepal:

In August 1854, Jang asked me to prescribe for one of his wives, daughter of the ex-Raja of Coorg, who was very ill. I declined doing so, unless I saw the patient. He then allowed me to see her. Her apartments are low, narrow, passage rooms, and she was lying on a mattress-bed on the floor, with a slave-girl using a hand-punkah over her. Her hair was unconfined, and loose over her shoulders. On the second visit, I opened a large abscess on her right side, much to Jang's delight and the astonishment of his own two native doctors, who were present. On her being a little faint, I told them to give her a little water; while she drank it, I had to stand up in the sill of an open window, looking into the Court, so that my feet might not touch the drugget, or any part of the furniture directly or indirectly connected with her bed, although two minutes before there was no objection to my feeling her pulse, and examining and lancing her side—a regular case of swallowing the camel and straining at the gnat...

Gangamma gradually recovered her health over the years, and blossomed to be one of the favourite wives of Jung Bahadur. Colonel G. Ramsey, the Resident at Kathmandu, in a letter to Sir John Login dated 28 November 1860, wrote about Princess Gangamma, and expressed his surprise at the marriage of Princess Gowramma and Colonel Campbell:

> ...Pray offer my best regards to Lady Login. That is surely not a brother of hers who married the Princess Gouramma of Coorg the other day! Her sister, who married Jung Bahadoor some years ago, is now a fine looking young woman, and seems happy enough. The other sister, whom he also brought with him in 1858, was sadly duped, and wanted to go back to her brothers. She is said to be very unhappy – at least, she was some months ago, but I have not heard of her lately...

Gangamma was educated in Nepalese since her arrival a Kathmandu in 1851, and she now spoke the language fluently Like Gowramma, she too had lost touch with her own mothe tongue. It was with much difficulty that she carried on conversation with her mother Subadhramma and other members of the famil whenever she visited Benares.

Jung Bahadur had visited Coorg Nest with Gangamm during the winter of 1858 to offer help to Veerarajendra family. During his meeting with the wives, sons and daughte of the raja, Jung Bahadur's eyes fell on Muddamma, a young half-sister of Gangamma. When the family complained abo their financial difficulties, he offered to help the family, but return wanted Muddamma as his wife! The raja's family, in di straits at the time, agreed to the proposal. Once in Kathmandu, Muddamma was extremely unhappy in the over-crowded zenana of Jung Bahadur. After enduring her misery for more than a year, Muddamma insisted on returning to Benares. Seeing her sister suffering, Gangamma intervened; Jung Bahadur bowed to his favourite wife's insistence and Muddamma rejoined her family in Benares. Muddamma soon found a suitor from a royal family. She married Raja Raghubir Singh Judeo of Maihar in Central India. An elder sister, Veeramma, married a rich *jamindar*, the Deshmukh of Bodhan province, near Secundrabad. Veerarajendra's sons tried to enter into alliances with brides from their father's erstwhile kingdom. However, their overtures to marry brahmin and Coorg girls from Kodagu were spurned. In Kodagu, there was no sympathy for Veerarajendra and his family.

In London, Gowramma was leading a secluded and lonely life. She often reflected what it would be like to meet all her half-brothers, half-sisters and stepmothers. She realised that they spoke different languages now and would find it difficult to even communicate. Colonel Campbell often asked her for money, and would stay away from home for several days. He had also taken to spending more time with his grown-up sons. Gowramma very much wanted to improve her relations with her husband and had to persuade him to visit Rome as a family, a dream she had long cherished. However, Colonel Campbell was non-committal and did not return Gowramma's overtures.

Unaware of the reality, Queen Victoria was pleased that her goddaughter Gowramma had finally found happiness and was content with her child. She planned to invite the princess and Colonel Campbell to one of the functions in the palace. The Queen was also keen to see Gowramma's daughter. Unfortunately, in December 1861, the queen suffered a great catastrophe when Her Majesty's consort and love of her life, Prince Albert, suddenly took ill. He was diagnosed with typhoid, which was attributed to the poor hygienic conditions in Windsor Castle. His condition worsened, and in spite of the efforts of the best of doctors, Prince Albert died on 14 December 1861. Queen Victoria was devastated; she withdrew from the public and remained in seclusion for the next seven months. The queen took to dressing in black ever since her widowhood. She was next seen in public only in July the following year, at the wedding of her daughter Princess Alice.

Gowramma continued to maintain a brave front despite her husband's indifference towards her and her child. She took on all the responsibilities of bringing up her daughter who was now more than a year old. However, to make matters worse, recurrence of the debilitating cough began to trouble her again and she often felt weak and sickly.

Things took a turn for the worse when one day, Colonel Campbell suddenly ordered her to show him the jewels that were Veerarajendra's legacy to Gowramma. Alarmed and intimidated, she fetched the red satin sachet and showing him the contents, nervously said, 'I want to preserve these valuables for our Edith.'

'Yes, of course,' the Colonel responded rather brusquely.

From that day onwards, Gowramma kept the red satin sachet close to her. She realised that the Colonel was a spendthrift with expensive tastes. He was a regular at the races where he won and lost large sums of money. Physically too, she did not feel well and tired easily. She maintained regular correspondence with Lady Login and they met occasionally. The Logins adored the talkative little niece Edith.

Sir Login and Lady Login were worried about Gowramma's health. The princess showed symptoms of tuberculosis, the dreaded disease. Even though outwardly she seemed deceptively healthy, they knew all was not well with Gowramma. 'Princess, you need to take every precaution concerning your health,' the Logins advised her. Gowramma responded by pleading, 'Should anything happen to me, you will take care of my Edith, won't you?' Lady Login also sensed that the relationship between Gowramma and her brother was strained. After a brief period of happiness, Gowramma's life had plunged into a state of despair.

In December 1862, Sir John Login made a brief visit to India, on a request from the Board of Indian Tramways Company, in connection with the establishment of railways in Bombay residency. He promised Gowramma that he would look up her family in Benares. By the time he completed his assignment and wanted to tour Lucknow, Fatehgarh, Benares and Calcutta, it was summer. Not in the best of health, he could no longer tolerate the heat and decided to sail back home. Dr Login was particularly keen on visiting Fatehgarh, but had to be satisfied with reports gathered by the local British administration. He managed to get news about Gowramma's family from his friends in Benares. When he returned to England in April 1863, he had plenty of news for Maharaja Duleep Singh and Princess Gowramma.

After his return from India, Sir Login decided to retire from active duty. He was not in the best of health. In June 1863, the Logins shifted to a seaside residence at Felixstowe, on the Suffolk coast. They continued to take interest in the affairs of Duleep Singh and Gowramma. Duleep Singh, by then, was at loggerheads with the India Office and the governor-general, regarding the quantum of allowance he was to receive. What enraged the maharaja was the unrelenting stand of the government that his sons would not inherit his properties in England after his demise.

Duleep Singh's mother, Maharani Jindan Kaur, had accompanied him to England after his visit to Calcutta in 1861. She was almost blind and in poor health. After 1849, Lord Dalhousie had seen to it that she was kept away from her young son. In her old age, she was happy to be reunited with her son after more than ten years of forced separation. Sir Login was uneasy about Duleep Singh spending too much time with his mother who he was sure would undo the Western values painstakingly instilled in the maharaja. He tactfully arranged for a separate accommodation for the maharani and her servants at Lythe Hall in the neighbourhood of Mulgrave. The cold, wet and foggy weather in London did not suit Jindan Kaur but she endured the discomfort to be close to her only son. After enduring the weather and ill-health for two years, she breathed her last on 1 August 1863. By then she had influenced her son sufficiently against the British for usurping their prosperous kingdom. Duleep Singh was profoundly influenced by his mother's assertion of a prophesy: that he was destined to be the next Sikh Guru—the eleventh—and that he would regain his lost kingdom, and more.

Her dying wish was to be cremated in India and her ashes immersed in one of the holy rivers. But the Indian government vacillated again about allowing Duleep Singh to travel to India with his mother's body. Sir Login, despite his indifferent health, came to London to help and advice the maharaja. It was decided to temporarily intern the mortal remains of the maharani in an unconsecrated vault in Kensal Green Cemetery, as was done the case of the ex-raja of Coorg. The India Office was wary of

Duleep Singh visiting India, lest his presence became a rallying point for the Sikhs.

Princess Gowramma invited Sir and Lady Login to celebrate her daughter's second birthday on 2 July 1863. Gowramma made Sir Login tell her once again about Benares and news of her family. For the first time since coming to England, she felt nostalgic about her carefree days in Coorg Nest. She wished she could play holi with Edith. But it was a 'heathen' ritual she had given up many years ago.

Lady Login, herself preoccupied with Sir Login's poor health, made anxious enquires about Gowramma's physical condition. The princess looked weak and listless. Gowramma tearfully confided to her sister-in-law, 'I am haemorrhaging again. Quite often, when I cough, there is blood. I am worried for Edith should I be called to the Lord.' Lady Login tried to comfort her as best as she could. Colonel Campbell, who was present, assured that his young wife was getting good medical treatment and there was no cause for worry.

Meanwhile Sir Login's health showed signs of improvement after their shift to Felixstowe. Living by the seaside seemed to revitalise him. But it was short lived. On Saint Luke's Day, the family attended mass, and Sir Login was in good spirits. In the evening, the family and the household sang their favourite hymns together. After supper, he retired to his room upstairs, humming, 'Jesus, the lover of my soul.' But he suddenly took ill and passed away before his wife could call for help. Sir John Spencer Login was aged fifty-four.

Sir John Login's sudden demise was an enormous blow to both Maharaja Duleep Singh and Princess Victoria Gowramma.

The doctor and Lady Login had played crucial roles in the lives of these two Indian royals. At his mentor's funeral, Duleep Singh lamented, 'Oh, I have lost my father—for he was, indeed my father, and more than my father.'

Princess Gowramma, by then frail and almost bedridden, could not attend the funeral. She wrote an emotional letter to Lady Login condoling Sir Login's passing:

27, PORCHESTER TERRACE,

October 21, 1863.

My Dearest Lena,

I cannot express how truly distressed I am to hear of the sudden death of dear Sir John. I loved him better than any relations I ever knew, and I never can forget his kindness to me. I deeply feel for you, my dearest sister. I love you more than I ever did since you have written me that kind and affectionate letter.

I am much better than I have been, though still very weak, and the sad intelligence coming on one so unawares has made me feel still weaker, and my ideas so confused that I don't know how to express myself. May God bless you and give you comfort in your great sorrow, my dearest sister! John [Campbell] is much grieved, and sympathizes with you most deeply. I am so much distressed I can write no more.

Believe me ever your affectionate sister,

Victoria Gouramma

Lady Lena Login was greatly disturbed after receiving this letter from Princess Gowramma. She realised that the princess was in great distress and needed to be comforted. Despite being in mourning, Lady Login decided to visit Gowramma and her little child.

Aware of the visit, Gowramma dressed in the deepest of mourning attire, and eagerly awaited her sister-in-law. Even though she had got out of bed with great difficulty, she received Lady Login in the drawing room. She had dressed little Edith too in black from head to foot. Lady Login was overwhelmed at Gowramma's emotional outpouring. The princess seemed helpless and was clearly close to death's door. The dreaded disease had taken a firm hold on her.

Lady Login immediately informed Sir Charles Phipps of Princess Gowramma's failing health. Queen Victoria was immensely concerned and saddened by the prognosis. She wanted to know from Lady Login if Princess Gowramma could meet her either at Windsor Castle or at Osborne House. But Gowramma's condition had worsened and she could get out of bed only with the help of her maidservant. Gowramma fervently hoped that her health would improve and she could have an audience with Her Majesty. She yearned to show her daughter to her godmother. Gowramma's ill-health had prevented her from attending the wedding of the prince of Wales on 10 March 1863. Earlier, her difficult pregnancy had come in the way of her taking part in the wedding of Princess Alice on 1 July 1861.

Sir Charles Phipps wrote a letter on 27 October 1863 on behalf of Queen Victoria, offering Her Majesty's deepest sympathies to Lady Login on her bereavement. Sir Phipps wrote again the next day informing Lady Login of the queen's concerns regarding Princess Gowramma's health:

Windsor Castle,
October 28 1863

My Dear Lady Login,

I had written, but not sent, the accompanying letter by the Queen's command, when I received yours this morning. I feel very strongly the kind exertion you made in writing to me, and I pray God may strengthen and support you! You cannot overrate the regard I had for my dear friend, your husband, and my admiration of his character. I am very glad to hear that the Maharajah has shown so much feeling of the debt of gratitude which he owed to his kind and gentle, but always honest, mentor; it will, indeed, be a terrible loss to him, for Sir John always told him the truth, and gave him the sincerest advice. The Queen read your letter with the greatest interest. If there is anything kind from Her Majesty that I could say, and have not said, I have so far gone within Her commands!

The Queen has been very sorry to read the account you gave of Princess Gouramma's health; she wishes to know whether you think that it would be injurious to her health to come down here to see Her Majesty? The Queen does not forget the kind manner in which you and Sir John undertook the care of this poor child, at great personal inconvenience. If it is too much for you to write and answer this yourself, pray ask your daughter to do so.

Always, sincerely yours,

C.B. Phipps.

11

DEATH OF A PRINCESS

PRINCESS GOWRAMMA'S RAPIDLY deteriorating health was a matter
of concern to the queen, who asked Lady Login to send her
regular reports of the princess's condition. Gowramma's health
continued to decline, though there were brief respites when she
seemed to improve. Lady Login visited her often and stayed with
her whenever possible. The doctors attending on the princess were
not hopeful about her recovery. Gowramma wrote her last letter
to Lady Login on 15 January 1864 from her bed.

Whenever Lady Login visited, Gowramma would plead with
her sister-in-law to promise that Edith would be raised by her along
with her own children, until she came of age. 'Please promise me,
my sister, that you will look after my Edith,' Gowramma would

repeatedly beseech Lady Lena Login. It was heart-wrenching for Lady Login to see the ailing Princess and her helpless little girl. Colonel Campbell, however, kept assuring that he would take good care of their daughter.

Queen Victoria continued to worry a great deal about her goddaughter. Sir Phipps sent a telegraph to Lady Login at the queen's behest:

Osborne,

17 Feb 1864

My Dear Lady Login,

The Queen was very much grieved at the account you gave of the poor little Princess in your letter, and directed me to telegraph at once to inquire in Her name.

It is very sad to see one so young cut off, but I think you have long thought that her lungs were in a very unsatisfactory state.

I shall be greatly interested to see the sketch of the monument [for Sir Login], which you and the Maharajah have approved, and when I go to London shall certainly go to see the model. There has rarely lived a man with a more extended and pure benevolence, and I have certainly learned more of India, and Indian affairs, from him, than from any other man.

I fear, from what you say, that Princess Gouramma is in a very dangerous state. . . The dear Maharajah is not always very wise in his decisions, and I fear there is nobody now who has much influence over him. He must miss his faithful Thornton, too. I suppose there is no doubt about his going to India, as you say he intends doing?

Very sincerely yours,

C.B. Phipps.

The last days of Gowramma were painful for her and those around her. On 30 March 1864, Princess Victoria Gowramma succumbed to her battle against tuberculosis. She was a few months short of her twenty-third birthday.

Thus ends the tale of Gowramma—the quintessential destiny's child. She was the first Indian princess to land on British soil, the first Indian royalty to embrace Christianity, and the first goddaughter of Queen Victoria from the Indian colony. Her Majesty mourned the death of Gowramma, and at Osborne House, a red rose was placed on behalf of the queen near the painted marble bust of Princess Victoria Gowramma sculpted by Baron Carlo Marochetti.

Princess Gowramma was buried in Brompton Cemetery in London. In April, the queen expressed her intention to have a suitable marble memorial erected at her grave. Sir Charles Phipps wrote to Lady Login echoing Her Majesty's wishes:

Her Majesty thinks a marble or granite cross would be the most appropriate, and hopes that, in the inscription, the fact of her having been godmother to the poor Indian child, may not be forgotten. No one knows better than you what deep interest the Queen took in her welfare. ... 'I cannot help thinking of her,' interjects Sir Charles in the message, 'with the melancholy look which she had, poor thing, when I went down to see her ill and unhappy at the Harcourts'. Still, it is a blessing that she is at rest, and that she was, by your brother's goodness, enabled to die in the hopes of a Christian. I send you the drawing suggested. ...' Again, later, I submitted ... to the Queen the enclosed draft for the inscription on the monument, of which H.M. approved, but said that a text must be added. . . The Dean of Windsor . . . has not yet found what he likes. ...

Of course, the enclosed inscription is only a proposal, and can be altered as Colonel Campbell likes. ... I should be very glad to hear that Colonel Campbell's petition was successful (for a continuance of part of the Princess's pension to her daughter), 'but I should rather be afraid the Secretary of State would consider the child as his [Col. Campbell's] and that they had done all that they could in giving the allowance for the poor Princess's life. There can, however, be no harm in trying, and it would give me great pleasure to hear of his success.'

Her Majesty the queen personally approved the draft of the words to be inscribed on Princess Gowramma's gravestone. The epitaph read:

Sacred to the memory of the Princess Victoria Gouramma daughter of the ex-Raja of Coorg, the beloved wife of Lieutenant Colonel John Campbell. Born in India, 4 July 1841. She was brought up early in life to England; baptized into the Christian faith under immediate care and protection of Queen Victoria, who stood sponsor to her, and took a deep interest in her through life. She died 30 March 1864.

'Other sheep I have, which are not of this fold' (John X, 16)

At the time of Princess Gowramma's death, Maharaja Duleep Singh was in India. After a long wait of two years for permission from the Indian government, he had finally set sail for Bombay in February 1864 with the mortal remains of his mother. Duleep Singh performed the last rites of Maharani Jindan Kaur according to her instructions. On 30 March 1864, the day Princess Victoria Gowramma breathed her last, Duleep Singh stood on the bank of the Godavari and consigned his mother's ashes in the swirling waters of the holy river. News of Gowramma's demise reached him months later at Cairo, where he had broken journey on his way back to England. He sent a telegraph expressing his sympathies to his friend Colonel John Campbell and goddaughter Edith Victoria.

The maharaja stayed on at Cairo for a few months to solemnise his marriage to the sixteen-year-old Bamba Muller, daughter of a German businessman and an Abyssinian lady. He had selected his future wife from the American Protestant Mission in Cairo, the school he had visited ten years earlier on his way to England. The marriage took place only on 9 June 1864 at the British Consulate at Alexandria, where the bride was recovering from a bout of jaundice.

In England, the maharaja's bride was described as of the same complexion as that of princess Gowramma but better looking and a size larger than the Indian princess.

12

EDITH—THE LITTLE VICTORIA

COLONEL JOHN CAMPBELL'S application to the India Office for
sanctioning a portion of Princess Gowramma's allowance for her
young child was rejected, as predicted by Sir Charles Phipps. The
India Office declared that it was the responsibility of Colonel
Campbell, as the father, to take care of the financial needs of his
child. Colonel Campbell, who was in grave financial difficulties
at the time, came to his sister Lady Login with a request to put
in a word to the queen. He expressed his inability to look after
his young daughter and pleaded with Lady Login to take care
of little Edith as desired by Princess Gowramma. Lady Login
was also the godmother of her niece. With great reluctance
Lady Login made a representation to the queen on behalf of her

brother for an allowance for Edith. Queen Victoria prevailed on the India Council, and an annual allowance of 250 pound sterling was granted to the three-year-old Edith Victoria Gowramma. The queen stipulated that Lady Login should receive the amount on behalf of the child. She also made it known that all the valuable gifts she had given Princess Victoria Gowramma should be secured for the motherless child.

Lady Login, who had been suffering from acute asthma, was advised by her doctors to spend the winter months for the next two years in the warmer climate of southern France. Colonel Campbell grudgingly agreed to look after Edith until his sister recovered. However, within a few months, Colonel Campbell handed over the child to an elderly couple named Bartletts at Rock Ferry, Birkenhead, near Liverpool. He was also in no position to retain their accommodation at Porchester Terrace. By the summer of 1867, when Lady Login informed her brother that she recovered sufficiently to take charge of Edith, he informed his sister that Edith was happy with the Bartletts and there was no hurry to shift her. Still recouping from her illness, Lady Login was rather relieved and postponed taking charge of Edith.

During this period, Colonel John Campbell met Lady Login a few times where he appeared troubled. Nevertheless, he kept assuring her that six-year-old Edith was growing well. His last visit to his sister, who was staying at Lancaster Gate at the time, was on 4 August 1867. They discussed various family matters and he once again assured Lady Login, who was keen on seeing the child, that there was no immediate need to shift Edith since the Bartletts were taking good care of the child. His eldest son, an Army Officer in India, had arrived in London on leave, and they were planning a family reunion. Lady Login noticed her brother clutching a black handbag. 'I am here in London on important business. I will be getting back to Kinloch in a couple of days,' he told her.

Colonel Campbell was staying in a lodging house on Jermyn Street in London. On 7 August 1867, he left the lodge, carrying the black handbag. That was the last anyone saw of Colonel Campbell. After waiting for about two weeks, his son and elder brother, General Charles Campbell, raised an alarm about his disappearance. He had not attended the family get-together. All he had left was a note for his son saying that he would be away on business for a few days. His brother and son were in a dilemma about reporting him missing to the police, since it was not uncommon for the colonel to be away on business for several days at a stretch. After three months, Scotland Yard was informed of the disappearance of Colonel Campbell. By then it was too late; the investigating agency could not find any trail. Colonel John Campbell had disappeared without a trace.

The Campbell brothers were well known in society. The Colonel's marriage to Princess Victoria Gowramma of Coorg had earned him a great deal of publicity. The mysterious disappearance of Colonel Campbell gave rise to many theories—it was widely believed that he had run away with his wife's valuable Coorg jewels in the black handbag. It was also speculated that he was on his way to Coutts Bank to place the treasure in a safe deposit vault, when he disappeared. The princess's jewels were never found. Foul play was also suspected, especially since Colonel Campbell was involved in the murky world of horseracing and betting. Another theory was that the colonel had left the country with the fortune to live abroad with a paramour. According to one rumour, Colonel Campbell had been kidnapped and murdered by some Indians, who were outraged that he had married an Indian princess.

Alarmed at the developments, Lady Login wanted to take immediate custody of her little niece. Besides being the orphaned child's godmother, she was also one of the legal trustees, along with Sir James Weir-Hogg. She had given her assurance to princess Victoria Gowramma and Queen Victoria that Edith would be brought up along with her own children. However, Lady Login faced an unexpected problem—the Bartletts did not want to part with the child. Having looked after Edith for nearly three years, they were deeply attached to her and wanted to be named the child's legal guardians. They called Edith affectionately 'Gip' for Gypsy! When this news reached the queen, she was shocked. Her Majesty was under the impression that Princess Gowramma's child was with Lady Login ever since the death of the Princess. Lady Login felt miserable for having neglected an important duty entrusted to her by the queen.

The Bartletts were elderly and childless. Mr Bartlett, a solicitor at Wolver Hampton, used all legal means at his disposal to prevent Edith from being taken away from them. He and his wife managed to prolong handing over Edith to Lady Login on one pretext or the other. Vexed by these delaying tactics, an exasperated Lady Login stated in court that under the circumstances she was not keen on assuming guardianship of the child. During the final hearing of the case in the court, the Lord Chancellor asked Lady Login whom she would recommend to take her place. She suggested her brother General Charles Campbell. However, after much contemplation, the Lord Chancellor passed an order on 12 November 1868 confirming that Lady Login, as an aunt and godmother, was the right person to be the legal guardian of the orphaned child. Happy that all the legal hurdles had been removed, Lady Login consented. She was asked to take custody of the child without causing trauma to the little girl.

Mrs Bartlett made yet another desperate attempt to evade handing over little Edith—she took the child away to the Continent. The court, however, took a stern view of this action. It was an illegal act, and tantamount to 'removing a ward from jurisdiction of the court,' a grave offence of which Mr Bartlett was well aware. The court passed serious strictures against the lawyer. Finally, a date was fixed for handing over Edith to Lady Login. When Lady Login's governess went to receive the child, she was told that Edith was down with 'scarlatina'. The residents of Rock Ferry including the local Vicar were disgusted with the Bartletts for their devious actions. The Vicar himself had seen the girl hale and hearty that very day. It was suspected that the Bartletts were interested in the 250 pound sterling annuity that was awarded to Edith.

Finally, when they found their Vicar and the neighbours turning against them, Mrs Bartlett saw the futility of her actions and came forward to handover Edith to the governess. The woman was truly fond of the child and it was an emotional parting. Mrs Bartlett was heartbroken and inconsolable. Little Edith, now about seven years old, was bewildered at the turn of events. Mrs Bartlett could not reconcile to her separation from Edith. Ever since the day Edith was taken away from her, Mrs Bartlett pined for her little 'Gip'. The intense grief finally took the old woman's life a month later.

The Bartletts had raised Edith in a very secluded environment. Except for the company of a pageboy, she did not have any companions her age. Her guardians had also not sent her t school. Lady Login was shocked to find Edith ignorant of basic alphabets though she spoke fluently. Dressed in drab ill-fitting clothes, Edith actually looked like a little gypsy.

Queen Victoria had sent word to Lady Login that she would like to see the daughter of Princess Gowramma. Lady Login requested for some time before presenting Edith to Her Highness. She wanted time to groom Edith and help the girl overcome some of the awkwardness in her behaviour. Edith, however, was a quaint and cheerful child despite her traumatic upbringing. Within a few weeks, Edith's demeanour changed and she was happy playing with children her age. In Lady Login's words, the little girl shed her 'dourness' with the attention given to her by the Login children. She had new set of clothes and looked pretty. After more than a month of tutoring, Lady Login felt Edith was ready to be taken for an audience with the queen.

Queen Victoria did not appreciate young children to be 'primed with proper speeches and drilled into rules of behaviour for their audience with her.' She preferred them to be normal and spontaneous. Hence, Lady Login decided not to reveal to the little girl the identity of the person they were going to meet. It was a delicate experiment, and she hoped the talkative little girl would not say or do something precocious.

On entering the queen's private chambers, Lady Login thought it prudent to meet the queen beforehand and warn her that the little girl was unaware of the identity of Her Majesty. The queen, who was in a relaxed mood, was quite amused and promised to overlook any mistakes by the young girl. She was intrigued by Princess Gowramma's child. She asked Lady Login to usher in little Edith Victoria Gowramma Campbell to her room. Just then two of the queen's daughters—Princess Louise and Princess

Beatrice—entered the room and were witness to what ensued.

Queen Victoria told her daughters that the little visitor was totally unaware of their true identity. She then beckoned Edith, 'Come here Victoria, tell me, do you know who I am?'

'No!' said Edith quite casually. The queen prodded her a little more. Edith blurted out, 'I suppose you are an old friend of my aunt's.' After a brief pause, she quite nonchalantly added: 'I have seen such a lot of them of late!' Everyone in the room held their laughter back and waited to hear more of Edith's innocent prattle. She was now comfortably sitting on queen's lap. Edith looked at the queen and continued, 'There was one very nice old lady she took me to see, who gave me a lovely box of sweeties!'

The little girl's hint was unmistakable, and the queen and her daughters burst out laughing. All the while the queen had been holding a gift box in her hand, and Edith was eyeing the present, waiting for the 'old lady' to hand it over to her soon.

The queen said: 'Oh, yes! Sweets would have been the right present for a little girl. But, Victoria, I have something else for you.' She then flipped open the box to reveal a beautiful crystal locket adorned with the royal monogram—VR.

'This will perhaps serve to remind you of this "old friend of your aunt's," said the queen, very graciously. 'Those are my initials. My name is Victoria too, the same as yours.'

'Oh, no, that cannot be, I know, I know!' retorted the small Victoria shaking her head vehemently. 'There is only one other Victoria, for my aunt told me so,' she said most reprovingly, and added, 'and she's the one we pray for in church!'

Everyone in the room doubled up with laughter. Edith's innocence had captivated the queen and her daughters. Edith met Her Majesty on two other occasions, the last being her forma presentation to the Royal Court when she reached the age of eighteen. The queen fondly remembered Edith's quaint banter during their first meeting.

Edith Victoria grew up in the Login home, where she lived until her marriage. On 5 October 1882, she married Captain Henry Edward Yardley of 4th Battalion, Royal West Kent Regiment. The bridegroom's father, Sir William Yardley, was the former Chief Justice of Bombay. The marriage took place in St Margaret's Church at Addington, Kent. Queen Victoria continued to take an interest in the welfare of Princess Gowramma's daughter. She always enquired about 'little Victoria' in her correspondence and meetings with Lady Login.

Edith Victoria had a happy married life. However, she regretted not knowing her mother about whom she only had faint memories. All she had to remember her mother were the Bible and the jewellery presented by the queen. There was an engraving of her mother's painting by Winterhalter and a few photographs. Lady Login had once taken her to Osborne House to see the marble bust of Princess Gowramma sculpted by Baron Marochetti. The beautiful, life-like sculpture of her mother moved Edith to tears. She had to hold herself back from hugging the bust of her mother. The disappearance of her father and the loss of the Coorg jewels bequeathed by her grandfather, also pained Edith a great deal. Fascinated by the account of India given to her by her aunt Lady Login, Edith fervently hoped to make a voyage to India to meet her mother's family in Benares.

Edith Victoria had a son named Victor Yardley. She was widowed in 1910. Victor followed his father's footsteps with a career in the army. He hoped for a posting in India and promised his mother that he would one day take her to Benares. However, this wish remained unfulfilled—Edith died in 1934 at the age of seventy-three. Unfortunately, two years after her demise, Victor met with a road accident while on duty in Australia and died in that country, thus bringing to an end the lineage of Princess Victoria Gowramma.

Veerarajendra's sons remained in Benares, where they married brides from local families. Over the years, their pension was progressively decreased. Faced with financial difficulties, they were forced to liquidate most of their heirlooms. Lady Login frequently received letters from them, or their agents, requesting her intervention in enhancing their allowances. In 1881, one B. Sheshagiri Rao from Secundrabad wrote on behalf of one of the sons of Veerarajendra named Somashekara. In Lady Login's *Recollections*:

> In April 1881, a most pathetic and quaintly-worded missive reached me from Secunderabad, written by one 'B. Sheshagiri Rao,' on behalf of Prince Somashekara Wadeer, and the family of the late Rajah. It reminded me of 'the parental affection and sincere feelings entertained by Sir John Login towards the family,' and stated that 'ever since the patron's demise the affairs of the family were ceased to bring forward,' and they were reduced to 'lowest ebb! Generally dependants appeal to the mercy of their mother, in the absence of their father,' the writer continues,'... I am impatiently waiting for motherly instructions! . . . I regret poverty is pinching at the Rajah's family; the maintenance was reduced for few rupees. ... If anything to be done for them, no other than yourself, Madam, are liberal enough to patronize. The good feeding given to the children by their mother shall be rewarded in double when they are successful (!!). I entirely depend on your early instructions.'

As I was at that date in constant touch with the India Office, I did my best to urge the case on their attention, but cannot tell, alas! whether my representations had any effect.

Lady Login lived to the ripe old age of eighty-four. She died on 17 April 1904, outliving both her Indian wards. Sir John Spencer Login and Lady Lena Login were few of the British of their time to have had close interactions with members of some of the royal families in India. Her memoir titled *Lady Login's Recollections,* compiled by her daughter Edith Dalhousie Login, gives a lucid insight into the life of the Indian royalty and the British officers in India.

Lady Login also authored a book, *Sir John Login & Maharaja Duleep Singh,* in 1890 to dispel some mistaken notions about her husband's role in raising Maharaja Duleep Singh. Lady Login's proximity to Queen Victoria throws light on the extraordinary affection Her Majesty bestowed on her goddaughter Princess Victoria Gowramma, and Maharaja Duleep Singh.

In the end, both Princess Victoria Gowramma and Maharaja Duleep Singh disappointed Queen Victoria. The grand plan for the colony through the union of the two Indian royals did not work out the way the queen and some of the high-ranking British officers had envisaged. The history of India would perhaps have been dramatically different had this scheme worked. A successful marriage between Gowramma and Duleep Singh could have encouraged many more members of the Indian royalty and subsequently their subjects, to embrace Christianity. It was argued that in the long term, religion was a more potent weapon to control those colonised, than the use of might.

When after a protracted struggle, Duleep Singh could not get his dues from the government of India, he turned against his sovereign, and on one occasion even called Her Majesty 'Mrs Fagan'—receiver of stolen goods! Queen Victoria, by then crowned the Empress of India, brushed aside the snide comment and did not hold it against her prodigal ward. In his desperation, the maharaja requested Queen Victoria to pay him the value of the Koh-i-noor diamond from her private funds. The queen, who was still very fond of the maharaja, was persuaded by her advisers not to consider this request lest it open a Pandora's Box of similar claims from other princes in India.

Duleep Singh fought a losing battle with the India Office to get his dues. He felt cheated, teased and humiliated. Twice married, he had three sons and five daughters. Queen Victoria was the godmother to his eldest son, who was christened Prince Victor. Surprisingly, none of his children had any offsprings. His profligate lifestyle got him into serious financial problems, and during his last days, he was hopelessly in debt. Betrayal by the government of India and the inability of Queen Victoria, even in her capacity as empress of India, to exert pressure on the India Office broke his spirits. Disillusioned, he renounced Christianity and reverted to the religion of his birth. His hatred of the India Office became so intense that he planned an outlandish proposal with the Russians to liberate India from the clutches of the British. His attempt to return to India were rudely prevented by the British. After suffering two debilitating strokes, Maharaja Duleep Singh died alone in a hotel room in Paris on 22 October 1893, at the age of fifty-five.

REFERENCES

1. *Coorg and its Rajahs, By an Officer formerly in the service of His Highness Veer Rajunder Wadeer, Rajah of Coorg*, Published by John Bumpus, London, 1857.

2. *Lady Login's Recollections*, By Edith Dalhousie Login, Published by Smith Elder & Co., 1916.

3. *Sir John Login & Maharaja Duleep Singh*, By Lady Lena Login, Published by WH Allen & Co., 1890.

4. *Sketches from Nipal*, By Henry Ambrose Oldfield, M.D., Vol. 1, Published by WH Allen & Co., London, 1880.

5. *Private Letters of the Marquess of Dalhousie*, Edited by JGA Baird, Published by William Blackwood & Sons, 1910.

6. *Queen Victoria's Maharaja—Duleep Singh*, By Michael Alexander & Sushila Anand, Published by Phoenix Press, 1980.

7. *Kodagina Ithihasa*, By DN Krishnayya, Published by University of Mysore, 1974.